By John P. Marquand

Life at Happy Knoll

JOHN P. MARQUAND

Life at
Happy Knoll

Drawings by John Morris

Boston · Little, Brown and Company · Toronto

ALL OF THESE PIECES FIRST APPEARED IN *Sports Illustrated*. THE
AUTHOR IS GRATEFUL FOR PERMISSION TO USE THEM HERE.

Contents

Life at Happy Knoll

CHAPTER I

Happy Happy Knoll

*A letter from Mr. Bob Lawton, Chairman
of the Emergency Membership Drive Committee of the Happy Knoll Country Club, to
Mr. Jeffrey P. Cutbutton, a new resident in
its vicinity.*

DEAR JEFFREY CUTBUTTON:

The whole "Welcoming Committee" of the
Happy Knoll Country Club have asked me as their
chairman to extend their thanks for our wholly delightful visit yesterday afternoon at your new home
and especially for the opportunity to meet your
charming family. In fact, you made us feel so at
ease that I am not sure on looking back whether I
made it quite plain that the Happy Knoll Welcoming Committee is only a sort of "gag." We are naturally Happy Knoll enthusiasts, but forget all about
it, and thanks for the wonderful time. However, I
am glad we got to you ahead of the Hard Hollow
Country Club crowd — not that we aren't all the

best of friends, and our annual golf meet with the Hard Hollow team is always a very happy occasion.

Seriously, Jeffrey — and one of the most warming things about our visit yesterday was that we moved so naturally into the first-name basis — everybody around here is overjoyed, not to say relieved, that you and Mrs. Cutbutton have purchased the Triboro Estate. Frankly, a lot of us who love this community were deeply worried when Arthur Triboro finally passed out of the picture. Of course, it is one of the star places in this community, but confidentially, we had been a little afraid that it might end up as a nursing home until you came along. I simply mean that the whole charming layout is pretty big for some people to swing, and it needed an imagination like yours to perceive that the kennels for the Irish wolfhounds could be made into a cozy sort of rumpus room.

As I say, we only dropped in to greet the Cutbuttons, but it is good news that you like golf, Jeff, and don't let me forget I want you to come to the next Saturday Golf Sweepstakes at Happy Knoll. It is swell, too, that Mrs. Cutbutton loves bridge, and I have made a memo to see that Mrs. Cutbutton is invited to the next Ladies' Bridge Lunch at Happy

[4   ]

Knoll. It was also great, Jeff, to see your lovely daughter. Our Janie is just your Myrtle's age. The two girls must get together "tout sweet" so that Janie can tell Myrtle about the teen-age Saturday dances at Happy Knoll — good, clean fun, and with sincere oversight. As for your sons, I hardly have to tell you what alert, manly little fellows they are! I can see them in my mind's eye on the Happy Knoll courts learning tennis from our Art Beckett. Art almost won the Intercollegiates and though older now, has retained a real sympathy for children.

Well, I seem to be getting back to Happy Knoll in spite of myself, envisaging the whole Cutbutton clan as members there, but my real point in writing is to confirm my offer of yesterday regarding assistance in helping you get settled. We both know how easy it is for anyone coming to a new area to get started off on the wrong foot, and here as elsewhere, all that glitters is not gold. The Hard Hollow crowd will surely have been to see you by the time you receive this letter. May I ask for your own sake that you won't forget your promise not to take any step in that direction without giving us Happy Knollers a chance to talk you out of it? I, frankly,

[5   ]

have no ulterior motives in this regard; though naturally Happy Knoll would be proud to include in its membership anyone able to swing the Triboro place, but that is not the point. The point is that I, as your friend and neighbor, don't want to see you getting off on the wrong foot.

Confidentially, when I first came here, a poor greenhorn from Greenwich, I was approached by the Hard Hollow crowd myself. I don't mean for a minute to be critical of Hard Hollow. They're a swell aggressive bunch and we here believe in cards face up and no throat cutting or subversion — not in this community. Still they do need new members very desperately at Hard Hollow, and I can imagine some of the exaggerated points they have made to you. One, no doubt, is the exclusiveness of Hard Hollow. Without meaning to be harsh, this theory is diametrically contrary to fact. The membership of Hard Hollow happens to be smaller than Happy Knoll's only because our community is not yet large enough to support two country clubs, and Happy Knoll is more popular but not for a single instant less selective. I might add as an ironical footnote that Hard Hollow's president, Gus Poultney — a prince of a fellow, by the way — just happened for

one reason or another not to make the grade when his name came up before the Happy Knoll admissions committee. No doubt Hard Hollow has its own standards. A great crowd, a swell place, *but it isn't Happy Knoll.*

They surely have also talked to you about charm and atmosphere. Well, their clubhouse is charming from the outside, all right, since there is a nostalgia about any ruin, not that they aren't still struggling pathetically to keep Hard Hollow up. Admittedly, the main room at Hard Hollow is said to have been constructed from the kitchen of the old Vanpoost farmhouse which stood there at the time of the Revolution, but anyone in this mid-century will tell you that the Hard Hollow plumbing is on the verge of collapse and cannot be fixed without tearing down the building. No wonder, with constantly recurring repairing crises, the deficit of Hard Hollow has reached unbearable proportions. No wonder they keep searching for new members.

Without wishing to be unkind to a delightful neighbor, what else has Hard Hollow got besides age? They may have weekly square dances in the old farm kitchen, but when the furniture is whisked away from our assembly lounge at Happy Knoll you have a modern ballroom that has been endorsed by orchestras of the Benny Goodman caliber, and only last year our ladies' committee has added a brand-new powder room. Another point they emphasize at Hard Hollow is the bar. Undoubtedly they will tell you that Henri, their barkeeper, is an acquisition from Happy Knoll. They are welcome to him. It is a well-known fact that one Happy Knoll Martini is equal to two of Hard Hollow's; and Henri, who has the bar on a concession basis, could doubtless tell you why. He did not need to tell us at Happy Knoll, where we have a magnificently alert house committee.

I am not a poet, except for writing a few well-received jingles at our annual banquets, but when it comes to comfort and lovely surroundings I could write an ode to Happy Knoll. Sit on our new flagstone terrace with a half-filled glass in your hand and look about you casually. The panorama greeting you spells, in a word, happiness and security. The first tee and the fairway leading from it form an inviting magic carpet, and our new pool right beside you is filled with happy, shouting children, supervised by Andy Muller who was an Eagle Scout before he tried out for the Olympics. Then comes the 18th green and next to it our four new *en tout cas* tennis courts resounding with the twang of rackets. The summer afternoon is waning. Happy voices drift from the bar and from the gin rummy players in the Pendleton Room. From the kitchen comes the tempting odor of French fries. Old Nicodemus, our chef straight from the Aicken Hunt Club, will be working on fried chicken in another minute. And what is this new sound? Cracked ice for juleps. Old Ned in *our* bar is making them up already for the thirsty foursome you see on the other side of the final sand trap. You say this sounds like any other country club? How wrong you are. *You have yet to know the warmth and charm of Happy Knoll.*

The Hard Hollow Committee must of course have emphasized their golf, since golf is frankly about all they have to talk about. Their tennis courts are negligible, their swimming pool an engineering fiasco; they have no winter skating rink, no skeet facilities — only golf. The Hard Hollow course is admittedly older than ours, as I am afraid is proved by the run-out condition of the fairways and the archaic drainage of the greens. They will also tell you about their pro, Jerry Scalponi, who by fast talk alone has convinced Hard Hollow that he is a teacher. If a good teacher is a poor player, then I admit he should be a professor. Our own Benny Muldoon at Happy Knoll has always "taken" Jerry on each occasion they have met, and Benny, though a fine sport, would not mind telling you, confidentially, what he thinks of Jerry. Personally, I would never let Jerry Scalponi analyze my golf swing. Only intelligent criticism or none is my motto.

Although I may be critical, I don't mean for a moment to discourage your joining Hard Hollow if you want to. There are many harum-scarum genial folk there with whom I have had many diverting, if profitless, hours. But in spirit Hard Hollow and Happy Knoll are divergent, and this is something to which anyone should give thought. Happy Knollers, like the Three Musketeers, are all for one and one for all; while there are mainly bitter individualists at Hard Hollow. There is good reason for this, I am afraid, since most of the members at Hard Hollow are business failures or well on the way to becoming such, and even their most influential members live on second-generation capital which they are consuming rapidly. The truth is that accumulation is neither practiced nor understood at

Hard Hollow. We have six topflight corporation lawyers at Happy Knoll; they have only one. Their only bank president is retired while we have three, all active. They have a newspaper columnist and an unknown short-story writer at Hard Hollow, but we balance them by two actors and top executives of six large advertising agencies. We also have a background of serious busy people, young folks, anxious to get ahead. That's why we have current events lectures at Happy Knoll.

Don't let them tell you about service at Hard Hollow, either, because it is nonexistent according to Happy Knoll standards. At Happy Knoll, Pierre Bedard, our house manager, has developed a real team. Our lovable employees are friends of all, as well as being real characters — from Algy in the dining room and Old Ned in the bar, right down to Old Tim who rules over the men's locker room. Don't try to tip any one of them, because they have learned to trust the Christmas Box. I might add, without wishing to be vulgar, that there is one simple step you might take before making up your mind on this vexed question. Walk around the parking space at Hard Hollow and then at Happy Knoll. You will note, incidentally, that the parking space at Hard Hollow, because of its seclusion, is hardly one to make careful parents happy about a daughter's dancing evening, but I am not referring to this detail, although I do think that any parent of a young girl would prefer Happy Knoll. Rather, I call your attention to the cars that are parked in both spaces. How many Cadillacs are there at Hard Hollow? Two, and the newest is three years old. How many at Happy Knoll? Eight on a summer's weekday and often twenty of a Saturday.

I do not say that such a detail should influence you unduly, nor do I mean that people who ride in Cadillacs are more socially congenial than those who drive lower-priced cars, but I do mean that the sight of a flock of Cadillacs is reassuring at a country club, when labor costs and everything else are on an upward curve. Incidentally, we have a little group here, just a few of us who are especially congenial, known as the Inner Sanctum Club, that meets in the bar each Saturday afternoon for a little bridge and a few stories. The crowd is particularly anxious to greet you, so how would it be if I called for you next Saturday? I was joking, of course, about the Cadillacs, but it would be nice to see another one in the circle off the drive.

It is conceivably possible that the tone of my letter could give you the impression that we, too, at Happy Knoll are competing for new members. Believe me, such an idea is contrary in fact. I know there is a rumor at Hard Hollow that we take in every Tom, Dick and Harry. I assure you that this also is not factual. As of today the waiting list is very crowded because our resignation percentage is fantastically small. Of course we can't — and won't — admit everyone, and each must wait his turn, but when we come across someone like you, Jeff, who can contribute so much in personality, good fellowship and in outstanding, successful character, we are resilient enough to make an exception. We don't have to guess — we know — that you're Happy Knoll material. I am so sure of it that the enclosed blank (which I hope you will fill out at once) is sheer formality. It will merely serve as a green light which will make me personally see that you are rushed through our admissions committee, which fortunately is having a special meeting next Wednesday. And believe me, we don't do this to everybody, Jeff.

Cordially yours,
BOB LAWTON

CHAPTER II

Deficit

*A confidential letter to Mr. Albert Magill,
President Emeritus of the Happy Knoll Country Club, from his friend, Mr. Roger Horlick,
member of the Board of Governors.*

DEAR ALBERT:

All the old crowd were in the men's bar last Saturday afternoon. The bad weather had kept the
newer element out of the place so that we were able
to discuss the personalities of certain fellow members with such freedom that several of us wished
verbally that you might have been with us. By the
way, I am afraid it will not surprise you to learn
that there is going to be another deficit this year,
and the time is drawing close when we shall again
have to pass the hat.

I know very well what you are going to say, because you have said it year after year and so has everyone else who has been approached on these un-
happy occasions. You are going to say there are a

whole lot of richer people than you in the Happy Knoll Country Club. You are going to say that you are sick of being a jolly good fellow carrying a burden which should be more evenly distributed among

a lot of other people you can mention, and then as always you will bring up Mr. Hugo Lassiter of Lassiter, Briscoe, Bevins, Inc., outdoor advertising specialists, in case you have forgotten his firm's purpose. You will say, why, specifically, did we ever take Lassiter into the club, especially when we knew all about Mrs. Lassiter, who, by the way, has again behaved very badly at the St. Valentine's Day Dance? Mr. Lassiter, you will be right in reminding us, was elected to membership largely because we hoped we could interest him in the welfare of Happy Knoll. Well, as of now we have not been able to interest Mr. Lassiter, although a lot of time has been devoted to the effort. It seems that presidents of advertising agencies have developed an even greater skill than presidents of other corporations for taking in money and never giving it out. Furthermore, it appears that some of the very ablest — and don't tell me that Mr. Lassiter isn't able — still believe that if you look out for the pennies the dollars will look out for themselves. I know what you are going to say. You are going to say that this old adage is no longer true under the present confiscatory income tax. I advanced the same thesis to Lassiter only the other day when he was using the club stationery in the Pendleton Room for semi-business correspondence, but he did not agree. He said that even in the ultimate tax bracket one can save a cent or two on the dollar and if you save the pennies the dollars look out for themselves. Frankly, Mr. Lassiter further practices this philosophy by availing himself of Happy Knoll to the uttermost, using all the varied hair lotions in the men's locker room, according to Old Tim, the attendant, and also four bath towels after every golf game. He will be approached again of course.

At 6 o'clock promptly the members of the Board of Governors, all six of us, adjourned from the bar to the Pendleton Room for the customary mid-month meeting. Since a number of decisions had to be made, the session was livelier than ordinary. The proceedings were complicated by our finding a new member from Foxrun Road, a Mr. Bert Byles, whom I do not think you have met, asleep on the leather-upholstered sofa that stands in the trophy corner. It had been rumored in the bar that Mrs. Byles had been trying to reach him by telephone all afternoon. He was very hard to arouse, but when on his feet was most apologetic. He said he was humiliated to be found asleep and that he would like to explain the circumstances since he was a new member who valued every moment he spent at the Happy Knoll Country Club. He had simply come to the Pendleton Room for a little quiet thought after lunch and must have dropped off. The week had been difficult for him in a business way, what with one thing and another, and also there were personal

difficulties, but he did not want to bore the Board
of Governors with his personal troubles. He never
wanted to bore anybody and he knew we were busy,
but he did have personal troubles. He wanted to
know whether Mrs. Byles had been trying to get
him on the telephone and when he was told that a
search had been made for him and that he could not
be found, he shook hands with all of us and thanked
us very much. Then he went on to say that the
Happy Knoll Country Club was beginning to mean
more and more to him each hour and minute. He
was beginning to love everyone in Happy Knoll.
The truth was that men at Happy Knoll understood they had to stick together. He did not want to
interrupt us because he knew we were busy, and at
the end of ten minutes he left in a very gentlemanly
way.

Hank Stevens raised the question, as soon as Mr.
Byles had left, as to who had proposed him for the
club, and no one at the moment could remember.
Then Hank said, as he usually does at our meetings,
that something more should be done about "alert-
ing" the Membership Committee. Then Tom Gaspell said that we should remember that we were trying to increase, not decrease, the membership of

Happy Knoll. Without a new drive and a substantial increase in dues, how could we add to the watering system on the golf course and build two new tennis courts and employ a swimming instructor and improve the squash courts? Happy Knoll was a recognized and integral part of our suburban community. The community was growing and attracting newer and livelier types each year and there was nothing wrong with this new member, Byles, except that he had gone to sleep, and sleep was a physical necessity for everyone at some time or other. And by the way, before the meeting came to order, did anybody know about Mr. Byles' financial status, because if he loved everything so much he might be able to help with the deficit?

Then Bob Lawton took the floor before he was invited. I don't know how well you know Bob Lawton, but I personally don't think he should ever have been put on the Board of Governors. He is another of our advertising executives and consequently full of what he calls constructive and positive ideas. He said he knew Bert intimately, but then Bob Lawton knows everybody intimately. Bert had a lovely wife and two lovely young children who attended the Country Day School with his and Mrs. Lawton's

own children, as he put it. They had purchased a new house in the new development on Partridge Hill Road. Bert, he believed, was managing some accounts for Batten, Barton, Durstine & Osborn, or some firm in that category, but he would doubt whether Bert was in the $20,000 bracket as yet.

At this point Bill Jonas interrupted and I was very glad to have him do so.

"Then what are we wasting our time talking about him for?" Bill said. "We haven't got all night and we've got a lot of problems here. And the first one is that the deficit for our fiscal year is $15,000. How are we going to pay it?"

I know exactly what you are going to say, and it echoes the remarks of other Governors. You are going to say, How is it possible that this year's deficit could have risen so substantially above that of last year's, when last year's was the highest deficit in the history of the Happy Knoll Country Club? You know Bill Jonas. He always has the facts and figures and he produced a number of them immediately. I shall name only a few items.

Casual breakage at dances and other entertainments during the year, $1500. Casual breakage is somewhat hard to define. I gather it means damage not anticipated in the budget and losses which cannot be traced to careless individual members. For example, if a chair in the card room collapses because someone unduly corpulent falls upon it violently, as happened four times last year, it is hard to blame either the chair or the player, since our furniture is not as young as it used to be. Then there is the new flagstone terrace. Glass and china fall on it inevitably, and the terrace unfortunately is situated near the new coeducational bar.

A settlement of the foundations under the kitchen, $4800. You may remember we have been warned about this for the last twenty-five years. The warning finally bore fruit the night before the Annual Dinner.

New floor for the Golf House, completely worn out by spiked shoes, $1500.

Addition to the Professional's guarantee, $1500. We can either pay this or lose Benny Muldoon, and you wouldn't want to let this happen, would you? Frankly, Benny has not been the same since he reached the third round of the National Open. You may recall I advised against getting a purse together and sending him there. The Hard Hollow Country Club has been after him ever since in a very aggressive and unsportsmanlike manner, and though Benny says he hates to make the change, he has two children and Mrs. Muldoon is expecting again.

It also seems there is a new kind of cutworm on the greens, but I shall not bother you about that.

The fact remains that our total deficit is $15,000. It was agreed that we would have to pay it somehow.

As I have said before, I don't know how well you know our new member on the Board of Governors, Bob Lawton, but I must say that he did come up with an amazing suggestion.

"Mr. Jonas," he said (it is nice to know that he still knows his place and still calls Bill Mr. Jonas), "of course I am speaking only off the top of my head, but this concept might have some validity. Has anyone given any serious thought, taxwise, to making Happy Knoll a tax-exempt institution? Of course I am only thinking out loud and at random, but such a situation would encourage potential dollars, contributionwise, wouldn't it?"

"Yes, it certainly would, Mr. Lawton," Bill Jonas said. "Have you got any thoughts from the top of your head as to how to make the Happy Knoll Country Club a tax exemption, taxwise?"

"I have no mature thoughts at the moment," Bob Lawton said, "because, very frankly, I am merely throwing out ideas for the rest of you gentlemen to kick around. But could there not be some way to set up the Happy Knoll Country Club as an educational institution?"

"How's that one again, Mr. Lawton?" Bill Jonas said.

"It surprises you, doesn't it?" Bob Lawton said, and he laughed in a very engaging manner. "Quite frankly, it surprises me too, now that I have tossed it off, but quite seriously, all good ideas are surprises at their inception, Mr. Jonas, before they are kicked around."

"All right," Bill Jonas said, "let's kick it around, Mr. Lawton. I don't see, seriously, as you say, how we can turn Happy Knoll Country Club as of this present date into a university."

"And if we could," I said, "it would have to be coeducational."

I thought this would close the subject, but then perhaps you don't know Bob Lawton.

"Now we're getting somewhere," Lawton said. "In my opinion there should be more women and children participation in the Happy Knoll Country

Club than exists at present, and I have some rather interesting ideas on the subject."

"God Almighty," Tom Gaspell said, "do you mean we ought to open a nursery school?"

"It really seems to me," Bob Lawton said, "that you have just made a very real contribution, Mr. Gaspell. A great many of the younger gals around here would appreciate leaving their children under supervised care so that they could brush up seriously on their golf and tennis and bridge. I can assure you that Mrs. Lawton would appreciate it, and when you come to think of it, why isn't a good bridge course educational?"

Bill Jonas looked for a few moments at Mr. Lawton. I know you admire Bill Jonas as much as I do, Albert. There always has to be someone to pull things together, and Bill Jonas generally can.

"Well now, Mr. Lawton," he said, "I find your suggestion interesting and I'm going to speak off the top of my head too. Very frankly, Mr. Lawton, this is one of the damnedest and one of the most daring concepts that I've ever heard advanced on these premises. It almost makes me believe that the Board of Governors of the Happy Knoll Country Club is on its way to joining the ranks of the intelligentsia, and don't think for a moment I'm speaking in the spirit of irony, Mr. Lawton, because I am not. I am very frankly impressed by your idea, if not taxwise, otherwise. I am an older man than you, Mr. Lawton, but not so old as to have been responsible for naming this place Happy Knoll. However, when I first joined here, this club had only a nine-hole golf course; the clubhouse was only a three-room unfinished building; there was no automobile problem, only a shed in which to tie up horses. Old Angus in the golf shop made his own woods and fitted hickory shafts to the irons. This obviously dates me, and we've grown since then, but in all those years I have never heard anyone advance your concept, Mr. Lawton.

"You are quite right, the Happy Knoll Country Club is indeed an educational institution. It is a laboratory of manners and social philosophy, and more damn things happen here than any place I know. God bless America for being able to supply places like Happy Knoll where we can express ourselves freely and kick ideas around. I am glad you have brought up this point, Mr. Lawton. Frankly, I have learned more at Happy Knoll than I ever did at Dartmouth. If Dartmouth is tax-exempt, so ought Happy Knoll to be; and President Eisenhower, as a golfer, should be interested. Yet, as a tax lawyer, Mr. Lawton, I can tell you that unfortunately there is no justice in Washington. They don't understand in the Bureau of Internal Revenue that the country club is a great American institution, yes, perhaps our greatest contribution to this century; and now, Mr. Lawton, if it's all the same to you, let's not come up with any more creative thoughts, but let us come to the business of this meeting. How are we going to pay the deficit?"

Well, Albert, there are economists, usually ones loyal to the Fair Deal, who tell us that financial health can be attained by consistently spending more than we make because all that we spend goes back into the economy. If this is true, the Happy Knoll Country Club is surely in a very healthy condition. The upshot of the meeting was that we must pay the deficit as we have before, not by raising the dues, but by asking a few loyal members to make an extra contribution. I have been deputed to inform you personally that you are down for $2000. Please send it as soon as possible so that you may have a happy summer at Happy Knoll, thinking of how you have added to the happiness of so many.

With all best wishes for a happy vacation,

As ever yours,

ROGER HORLICK

CHAPTER III
Breakage

A letter from Mr. Roger Horlick of the Board of Governors of the Happy Knoll Country Club to Mr. Albert Magill, its President Emeritus, regarding the coming-out party given on the club premises by Mr. and Mrs. Godfrey Bledsoe for their daughter.

DEAR ALBERT:

I am writing you in behalf of the Board of Governors to ask your help regarding a clash of personalities which at present is rocking the Happy Knoll Country Club. Our problem primarily has to do with Mr. and Mrs. Godfrey Bledsoe, whom you know better than I, and who yesterday were responsible for an emergency meeting of the Board. You are doubtless going to say that the Bledsoes are not the sort of people who could possibly cause such trouble. The Cromley crowd — who have been drinking even more over week ends than usual — perhaps. The Athertons and the rest of that married group who live in that Beaver Hollow development

[30]

— no doubt; but the Bledsoes — certainly not. I know that you will also say, don't under any circumstances antagonize Godfrey Bledsoe, because we hope he will help with next year's deficit. This is exactly why the Governors decided that you might care to write him personally instead of our sending him a more formal communication. I may also add, the feeling is unanimous that you should do this, since it was you who were recently most vocal in advising that the facilities of Happy Knoll should be thrown open to young people, and thus it is largely because of you that the Bledsoes used the club last Friday evening for the coming-out party of their daughter, Alicia.

I know you will say that you at least have not forgotten that girls will be girls and boys, boys; and that you can illustrate this by some stories of your own youth and mine which, frankly, are about as outmoded as a T-model Ford. I also recall distinctly how you feel about young Alicia Bledsoe, who is known to her friends as Allie. I recall, one afternoon last spring when we were sitting on the terrace by the new bar watching the young people disport themselves on the tennis courts, that your attention was so drawn to Allie Bledsoe that you expressed the wish that girls in our time had dressed more like her, since then the process of natural selection might have gone on in a more unimpeded manner. You then ended your statement by saying she was "well stacked up."

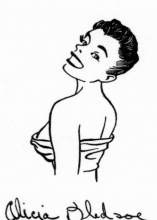

Alicia Bledsoe

I recall I told you to use the language of your age group and added that the younger generation were becoming a real problem at Happy Knoll. In fact, only that day Old Ned at the bar had suggested that it might be better at the young people's dances to serve young boys of fifteen slender shots of bourbon rather than to let them drink it privately behind the bushes of the parking area. This made you indignant. You said that you also had sampled alcohol when you were fifteen and if you were fifteen again you would repeat and do a lot more besides. It was a pity, you said, that we had not faced the problems of youth as frankly and fearlessly as young people do today. Also we must never forget that the younger generation is disillusioned and has lost its sense of security.

Frankly, Albert, I am growing a little weary lately of observing the lengths that young people now go in their search for security. I am also tired of hearing about "lost generations." If I remember rightly, this phrase started when a young man from Princeton, named F. Scott Fitzgerald, wrote a novel entitled *This Side of Paradise* in which he revealed that boys and girls, disillusioned by the antiquities of World War I, exchanged furtive embraces in their fathers' limousines. I reread this novel the other day and found it was very pallid stuff. Ask Allie Bledsoe if I am not right, or stay around for a while during one of our Saturday dances at Happy Knoll where Allie and her contemporaries are seeking for security.

Frankly, there was an unusually vigorous search

for security at Alicia's coming-out party the other night where the latest lost generation, in striving to find itself, not only broke plates, glasses and furniture, but stole various mementos. None of us would bother you about this if it had not caused bad feeling and high words among parents who are solid members of the club. Naturally high animal spirits should be discounted and so should a little malicious gossip. I can also agree that our young people today are under a strain of uncertainty, but I only wish they would remember that everyone else is under a similar strain, especially the Board of Governors of the Happy Knoll Country Club.

The Board resents being blamed for what happened last Friday night. It is not our duty to censor the manners and morals of dancing parties, which should be up to parents. The trouble is that parents also have become demoralized, especially at Happy Knoll. For example, in view of the complaints that were showered upon the Governors regarding events of last Friday night, it was necessary to conduct several purely informal investigations. In the course of these it transpired that several young people, who do not wish their names mentioned, distinctly saw young Willie Atherton enter the Pendleton Room,

go to the trophy corner and remove the silver polo mallets from the hands of the interestingly sculptured riders that decorate the top of the urn of the old Gibbs Polo Trophy that was won by Happy Knoll in 1887. On learning what had become of the polo mallets, we immediately communicated with Willie's father, asking that they be returned. Instead of being cooperative, he was furious, not at his son, but at the Board of Governors for insinuating that Willie should have committed such an act. It was also discovered that young Charlie Cromley stole the memorial portrait of old Jerry Farnsworth in his plus fours from the Pendleton Room. When Cromley Sr. was asked to have it returned, he, too, was furious. (The portrait, in case you are worried, has just been discovered in a drugstore window.) Then there was what is now referred to as "the scene" by the swimming pool which the Board of Governors decided not to investigate at all. Rumor has it that one of the Gridley sisters, whom you have always said were delightful girls, attempted a strip-tease act on the diving board and failed to complete it only because she fell accidentally into the water. Simply because of these rumors, Mrs. Gridley, who has always seemed to me formidable, is threatening to sue the Country Club for defamation of character. Bernice, she says, was pushed into the swimming pool by a young man from New Rochelle who should not have been at the party at all. Even so, Bernice did not remove a single stitch of clothing and Mrs. Gridley says that she can prove it.

Well, so it goes. These are only casual samples of a number of curious events that occurred last Friday night. Yet whenever anyone is accused of being concerned with these happenings, it seems that all our young of Happy Knoll are innocent children who scarcely touched a drop of the champagne that Mr. Bledsoe vulgarly offered them. It seems, however, that there were other sinister forces afoot — unidentified young men who crashed the party and in particular a tough and undesirable element from the Hard Hollow Country Club. These individuals, it seems, none of whom can be identified, were responsible for all pilferings and all disorders last Friday.

It was the hope of the Board of Governors that this situation could be unraveled at least slightly and that bills for breakage and damage would be cheerfully shared by various responsible parties. This, it appears, is not to be the case. It seems that your poor friend, Mr. Godfrey Bledsoe, must foot the bill alone, which is going to be unexpectedly heavy. This is why we are asking you to write a letter that will break the news to Mr. Bledsoe pleasantly. The suggested draft I enclose will be useful to you largely because of the information it contains. Please feel free to say what you like, but along these lines and in this spirit:

DEAR GODFREY:

I wish that I might have been with you and Bertha at the Happy Knoll Country Club the other Friday. I hear it was a delightful occasion and you know how partial I am to your Allie. Indeed, like the late Mr. Justice Holmes, I almost find myself saying, Oh to be 70 again! As you and Bertha have often heard me remark, boys will be boys and girls will be girls, no matter what steps one takes to prevent it, and I believe that Happy Knoll should have the accent of youth and would indeed be a sad place without it.

If the Friday night party got a little out of hand in the hours of the morning after, this was not your fault and should be attributed only to the informality of the times in which we live; and after all, what is a country club for if one cannot have fun in it? Your guests were checked from a list at the door; you cut down on the champagne supply at midnight and gave orders that none should be served after 2 A.M.; the club bar itself closed on the stroke of 2 A.M., and Old Ned, who has been a loyal Happy Knoll employee ever since the repeal of Prohibition, has been through enough merry occasions to warrant your trust in his judgment when he assured you that everything was under control and that you and Mrs. Bledsoe could go home. Old Ned, in making this prediction, could not be everywhere at once. In fact, no one can be everywhere at once at a gay debutante party. There was no reason for you and Mrs. Bledsoe to have known that your party was still continuing at about noon on Saturday. You were still asleep when Mr. Bedard, from the front office, attempted to communicate with the Board of Governors, who invited some of your guests, still in vestiges of their evening clothes, to leave the bar and swimming pool. The Governors want me to assure you that they did this with great reluctance because tolerance is one of our Happy Knoll watchwords.

However, it did seem by then that things had gone far enough. As always happens on such occasions, a few repairs must be made to furnishings and grounds and I am taking the liberty of listing some examples so that you'll not be too surprised when you get a final estimate.

1) Mr. Swivens's electric golfmobile was discovered in the course of the evening by some of your guests, said not to belong to Happy Knoll. It was run over the 9th, 10th and 16th greens, all of which will need renovation, and the vehicle itself

was abandoned on the 14th fairway, almost a total wreck.

2) The large Persian rug in the Pendleton Room was cut into narrow strips which were tied together to form a rope for a tug-of-war game on the tennis courts. The rug is beyond repair.

3) A more than ordinary amount of glass and silverware was thrown into the pool, necessitating a thorough cleaning.

4) A peculiar situation developed at the bar. Old Ned, whose eyesight is not what it used to be, has discovered a number of bar checks signed by Dwight D. Eisenhower, Douglas MacArthur and other notables. The total of these will be available shortly.

5) An unusual interest was taken in the club trophies. The Bradshaw Cup for women's singles has entirely disappeared, as has the Happy Knoll Bridge Bowl. The gold-plated figure of a golfer has gone from the top of the Happy Knoll Challenge Urn and the silver polo mallets have been removed from the polo trophy. These are small matters but will need prompt attention.

6) The customary allowance for wear, tear and breakage appears to have been inadequate. Two sofas caught afire, one by accident and one on purpose since someone, not a member of Happy Knoll, conceived the idea of building a bonfire to greet the sunrise. This fortunately was checked by Mr. Bedard, but not wholly in time.

7) Pete, the caddie master, who was kind enough

to help the house staff during the latter part of the evening, broke his arm in a friendly scuffle. It is doubtful whether this damage comes under the head of workmen's compensation.

There will be some other items, but I do believe that these are the main ones. We hope you will feel that they indicate that the party was a great success. It has already been termed one of the most active in the history of Happy Knoll, and one long to be remembered.

Sometime in the near future I hope you will tell me all about it yourself. As I say, I am deeply sorry not to have been present.

Cordially yours . . .

I think this is about the way the letter should be written. There is no reason for complaint and recrimination. A good-natured calling to attention ought to be enough. Frankly, the whole affair has taught us a great deal at Happy Knoll and we are already considering precautionary measures to be used in future festivities. Live and learn is always our motto, but please get your letter off as soon as possible and please let us know what reply you elicit.

With all best wishes for a continued happy holiday,

Yours, as always,
ROGER HORLICK

CHAPTER IV

The Way the Ball Bounces

*A letter from Mr. Roger Horlick of the
Board of Governors of the Happy Knoll
Country Club to Mr. Albert Magill, President
Emeritus, regarding the golf professional,
Benny Muldoon.*

DEAR ALBERT:

The Board of Governors at the Happy Knoll
Country Club faces a crisis right at the height of
our golfing season. It suddenly looks as though we
may lose our golf professional on a two weeks' no-
tice. I know what you are going to say. You are going to say that the Board voted another thousand
dollars for Benny Muldoon at one of their recent
meetings, and you are also going to say that we
should at least have tied Benny up on a season's contract. Well, I suppose you are right on both scores,
but still, facts are facts. We have never signed
Benny up on a contract because Benny has always
said he loved the Club and he has always seemed to
us like one of our members. Actually, one cannot
help being touched by Benny's reaction because he

seems more upset, if possible, by the prospect of im-
pending change than any of his host of admirers.

You know as well as I do that Benny is a senti-
mentalist at heart. There is a genuine quaver in his
voice when he speaks about the possibility of leaving Happy Knoll, which he says very frankly is his
second home. But, as Benny says, you have got to
face facts. It is like, he said when I interviewed him
yesterday, the time when he was playing his second
18 at Rough Briar in the State Open. He had belted
out a 300-yard drive right down the middle of the
fairway. There was quite a gallery following because, frankly, he was hot as a pistol right up to the
7th. There was the green, 80 yards away, heavily
trapped, but a cinch for a roll to the cup, if you
aimed for the upper slope. Would he use an eight-,
a nine-iron or a wedge? He had to make up his
mind. He must have been thinking about all his re-
sponsibilities there because he called for the wrong
club, landed in the trap and blasted out for a measly
four. So you have to make up your mind, and either
in match play or in life, making up your mind is
a pretty tough proposition. Come to think of it, as
Benny told me, and you know how philosophical
Benny can get when he has the golf house to him-

self, life from his experience is a good deal like a game of golf. You get yourself into the rough in life just the way you do when you slice off the tee and you've got to take a wedge and some religion to get yourself squared away. Just like in life, in golf you start out with nothing but you have to come home with something.

I took the liberty of interrupting Benny at this point, telling him that in golf the less strokes you came back with the better, and that in life, too, a large income is often a source of worry.

Benny said that at the same time you had to come back with something. And these days when he came back to Patricia (that's Mrs. Muldoon), Patricia didn't feel he was bringing home enough, even if life wasn't exactly like golf. It seems that Patricia has been needling Benny Muldoon ever since he won that State Open. I told you at the time, Albert, you never should have offered to pay Benny's expenses for that occasion, and if you hadn't, I don't believe that Patricia (that's Mrs. Muldoon) would have allowed Benny to take the money out of what he calls "the kitty" for any such long shot. After all, Benny always said, previous to the State Open, that he was a teacher and not a tournament player. Well, now it's different. Benny now wants to go out to California to Pebble Beach or somewhere so that he can slug it out with "the circuit," and Patricia (that's Mrs. Muldoon) has begun reading the sports columns, and if an unknown like Fleck could beat Hogan, why couldn't Benny beat Fleck?

It seems that Patricia is now making notes on the annual incomes of Hogan and a few others, and these figures prove that Benny is not coming home with enough. It seems that he is not thinking of the future of their two children and of the other that is on the way. Instead he only thinks about analyzing the golf swings of a lot of stingy though rich old loafers at the Happy Knoll Country Club. These are my words, not Benny's. These people, Patricia says, could never win the State Open and she could give any of them a stroke a hole and beat them herself if she weren't expecting. That's the way she is, pugnacious (I'm referring to Mrs. Muldoon). It seems that she keeps needling Benny. Only yesterday she asked him, now that he has won the State Open, why he can't go to a sporting goods store and get his name inscribed on a set of matched irons, like Mr. MacGregor? Ambition, it seems, is Patricia's middle name. It seems to me that Lady Macbeth displayed many of the same attributes on the evening that King Duncan dropped in for the night.

Well, as Benny said yesterday, that's the way the ball bounces and he is a family and not a single man and now there has come a crisis. Hard Hollow first made a bid for him and now comes Rocky River. Rocky River is willing to guarantee Benny two thousand dollars more than we are after we have met the Hard Hollow offer. Benny has been most honorable about it and is holding nothing up his sleeve because he loves Happy Knoll and everybody in it, but that's the way the ball bounces. Besides, if he turns Rocky River down, how can he tell Mrs. Muldoon? In addition, Rocky River has a golf house twice the size of ours and everybody at Rocky River loyally buys all their equipment from it. Benny doesn't mean to say anything tough about Happy Knoll members because he loves them all, but sometimes, just to save a buck, they do go to some cut-rate store in the city and come back to the Happy Knoll course with a lot of junk that he would be ashamed to handle, but that's the way the ball bounces. He has an ironclad guarantee that they never will do that at Rocky River, and they have a display room that can even handle slacks and tweeds besides caps and windbreakers. So here we have the question. What are we going to do about Benny Muldoon? I know what our deficit is, but Benny has been here for 10 years. A lot of people, including you, Albert, have to go to him regularly. How would you like it if you had to start with someone else? A golf pro, after all, is like a priest in a parish or a headmaster at school.

There are of course people who shop around among golf teachers, but these are hypochondriacs who can never cure themselves by advice from several sources. We both know this, Albert. You may recollect that some years ago I caught you sneaking out to the Hard Hollow Country Club to see whether their Jerry Scalponi could do more about your basic game than Benny Muldoon. I met you there because, frankly, I had come out for the same purpose and we were both agreed that all that results from promiscuous golf advice is unhealthy cynicism. Most professionals after diagnosing your golf ailments ask who taught you. When you tell them, they say it is too bad and all that can be done now is to start all over again and, by the way, your set of laminated woods are too heavy in the head and disturb your back swing.

The Way the Ball Bounces

I cannot bear at my time of life to face anyone else except Benny Muldoon, because he has a beautiful gift of sympathy and on the practice tee he suffers with me always. I admit it has been true lately, perhaps because Mrs. Muldoon has been suggesting that he underrates himself, that Benny seems to be cultivating a Scottish accent. The other day I thought I heard him say "Verra guid," but if Benny wants to be Sir Harry Lauder he still comforts me and leads me safely over the water hazards because his good words are with me; and I certainly ought to remember what Benny Muldoon has told me, because he says the same things over and over but then, what else is there for him to say?

You have got to be calm and collected, he says. Golf, if you will excuse his using a long word, is a psychological game. Have a mental picture in your mind, he says, of the right way of hitting through the ball and you can do it. Golf, if you will excuse his saying so, is a wee bit like religion, and a while ago a gentleman whom he doesn't think I ever knew, because Benny met him years ago at Hot Springs (but he was very important in the coal business and had a Rolls Royce and two lovely daughters) told him about a French doctor called M.

Cooey or something like that. You'll have to excuse his French, but seriously, this Doctor Cooey or however you say it stated that you simply had to say a couple of thousand times every morning, "Every day in every way I am getting better and better" and, believe it or not, you did. What Benny wants you to say is simply that every day in every way your golf is getting better. Say it two thousand times and then go out and see what happens. Only recently he made this suggestion to Mrs. Falconhurst. Benny was worried so sick about Mrs. Falconhurst that when he came home at night he couldn't eat. Frankly, Mrs. Falconhurst was a lovely lady, but he couldn't teach her to hit a balloon. But then he told her about this Frenchman and you ought to see her now.

Confidence is what you need in golf. If you want it in two words, confidence and Cooey is all there is. Now of course, Benny says, golf isn't like trying to bat a baseball or anything so easy, but in the end, like batting a baseball, it's confidence. Benny says he almost lost his confidence on the long 13th in the Open up at Rocky River. It was the afternoon round and something he ate wasn't sitting well on his stomach. He was using the two-wood on the fairway, giving it everything he had, and he might have even pressed but it was probably the frankfurter he had for lunch. Anyway, instead of making the green he hooked over the third bunker. Frankly, his knees sagged and he burst into a cold sweat, but he said to himself, "I can do it, I can do it," and he came across with the sweetest wedge shot of the day. It wasn't Benny who did it. It was Doctor Cooey and that's the way the ball bounces. As Benny says, there's some other things to golf. Sweep your club head low back on the ground, make a nice pivot, hit from the inside out clean, crisp and smooth. That's another little motto: be crisp and smooth, and let the club head do the work. Don't worry where the ball goes. Just do it and Benny will be happy. Just be crisp and easy and relaxed.

Well, I have been going to Benny more often I am afraid than I go to church. I have heard everything, and in fact I now know exactly what he will say next. In spite of Doctor Cooey, my reason tells me that my golf never will greatly improve and yet I do keep going back to Benny and so does everyone else at Happy Knoll. Why? I don't know any direct answer except that Benny can always make you feel that you're going to do better sometime in the foreseeable future. After all, as Benny said when I was speaking to him yesterday, golf teaching is like being a shill in a crap game. You've got to keep the customers coming, you've got to make them feel good and if you don't — no bottle for Buster.

Yet there is another, more cogent reason, I believe, that Benny is able to hold the large and captious public that he has at Happy Knoll. It is because he universally commands a deep respect. Somehow whenever I see Benny Muldoon I know I am in the presence of greatness. In a way he is more of a doctor than a teacher, but he does not need signed certificates nor garbled language to make his point. The tee-side is different from the bedside manner. The truth is, Benny always comes across. He can invariably chip to six inches of the cup. With his left arm alone he can send the ball two hundred yards. He can slice or hook at will and can parody the play of any of his pupils, but always in a genial manner. He can also drive a ball from the top of a gold watch without damaging its mechanism and once he was prepared to drive a ball off the head of our fellow member, Mr. Featherstone, who was in one of his customarily genial moods, but the Greens Committee intervened. I have always been sorry for this because it might have been that Benny would have hit below the ball for once in his career. Somehow when Benny Muldoon wears the golf accesso-

Benny Muldoon

ries that are on sale in the golf shop they always fit him; they never look ridiculous as they do on some of the rest of us — not the loudest shirts, not even tam-o'-shanters. But it is not dress, not exposition, but his unfailing kindness that I most admire. Benny knows very well that we could all be as good as he if we had had his chance to be a caddie at a New Jersey country club whose name I can never pronounce. He has a special niche in his heart for everyone, and a very long memory, too. It is true

that he asked me the other day how my water on
the knee was getting on, but he corrected himself
immediately. He had been thinking of Mrs. Falconhurst. He meant the bursitis in my right shoul-
der, the same complaint from which President Eisenhower suffers, and Ike is a pretty hot golfer,
considering. It is inconceivable to think of telling
any more intimate golfing troubles or the more dis-
graceful things I have done on the Happy Knoll
links to anyone except Benny Muldoon. There is a
personal rapport in these matters which cannot be
overlooked.

Frankly, Albert, I have not had a good year in a
business sense, but the stock market has been rising
in spite of the Fulbright Committee. I can, if necessary, sell something. There has been so much hat
passing lately that any more might cause repercussions. I think that you and I have got to take it
upon ourselves to fix this thing about Benny Muldoon. In fact, I have done so already. I have told
him that I would pay half and you would pay the
rest, and just remember, that's the way the ball
bounces.

Sincerely,
ROGER HORLICK

[54]

CHAPTER V

Should Auld Acquaintance Be Forgot?

A letter from Mr. Roger Horlick of the Board of Governors of the Happy Knoll Country Club to Mr. Albert Magill, President Emeritus, regarding the maintaining of the status quo of the men's bar and continuing the employment of its present barkeeper.

DEAR ALBERT:

As you know, there has been agitation recently, chiefly among the younger and less well-established members of the Happy Knoll Country Club whose names appear only too frequently on the bulletin board for nonpayment of house bills, to get Old Ned out of the men's bar at Happy Knoll and to renovate the whole place. The idea is, in accordance with the argot of a generation younger than ours, that the men's bar — where your father and mine used to have their toddies after a hard afternoon on the links — stinks.

Indeed, in a sense the men's bar does, in that almost two generations of excellent hard liquor have spilled upon its woodwork, creating an aroma which binds the past to the present. The word among several of our more successful young executives, however, is that the men's bar is archaic. They want the mirrors, the beer steins and the canvas of "The Frightened Nymph" by Bouguereau to be removed, and the bar and the brass rail and the two brass cuspidors along with them. In their place, they suggest something more like a Paris bistro or sidewalk café with high bar stools, artificial awnings and artificial sunlight. The clique that is most vociferous in demanding this change is headed by a young advertising man named Bob Lawton, whose election to the Board of Governors at Happy Knoll still remains to me a mystery. Granted that every element of our somewhat varied membership should, ideally, be represented, one must stop somewhere.

I don't know how well you know young Mr. Lawton, but probably very well if you have ever met him, because he is constantly thrusting out his hand and saying, "The name is Bob Lawton and it's time we got to know each other better." At any rate, it is the idea of our Bob Lawton to "live it up

a little in the bar." Primarily he proposes to have a
sign over its door called "Fun 'n' Games Room for
Men Only," and a scale of chromatic neon lighting
which will change at various hours and a number of

Bob Lawson

gambling machines arranged in what he calls a
"comedy manner," the proceeds of which will go
toward refurbishing the bar, which is now run at a
deficit. Without consulting anyone, he has already,
during a recent trip to Paris, collected some humor-
ous French drawings of a scatological nature as wall
decorations. The only one that I can now recall de-
picts a frightened dachshund looking at a wet um-

brella which is distributing a puddle on the floor. "Mon Dieu," the dog is saying in French, "they will think it is I."

But the thing that really upsets me is the move afoot to get rid of poor Old Ned, who, as barman, is the spirit of the place itself. It is said correctly that Ned, in spite of his almost forty years of loyal service at Happy Knoll, would never have been made head barkeeper here if Henri Racine had not been stolen under our very noses by the Hard Hollow Country Club. Old Ned is willing to tell anyone that he came to Happy Knoll as a local boy who did odd jobs on the golf course under Old Angus. He was admittedly never good with anything mechanical. Even today he often strips the gears of the electric mixer when he attempts to make a daiquiri. It is also true that Ned only became a barboy after he sprinkled salt on the 18th green, mistaking it for fertilizer. It is true that when Henri was abstracted in a most unsportsmanlike manner, Ned could not mix drinks as well as Henri. Indeed as of today if you ask for Scotch Ned is only too apt to give you rye, and he pours quinine water into highballs instead of soda. His eyesight is not what it used to be and his coordination, never good, has not recently improved. Annually he gets more flustered at Saturday night dances and he is more and more prone to leave the bar and let younger members take his place.

But none of this is really the point. The point to consider is the loyalty, the friendship and deep interest that Ned has always shown for every member of Happy Knoll for whom he has ever mixed a beverage, including that member's private life and his most confidential business affairs. Through the years Ned has developed an intuitive skill in estimating the incomes and inclinations of our members, and he is a walking encyclopedia about their pasts. Good Old Ned! I do not mean for a moment that he talks out of school. Up to date he is the most closemouthed individual in existence and under the proper circumstances will, I am sure, remain so. He has been and always must be a permanent feature of Happy Knoll. I frankly would not care to envisage my future or that of many others with Old Ned employed somewhere else, say in the bar or dining room at Hard Hollow.

You may think that I am implying that Old Ned is prying and inquisitive. I do not intend such a nonfactual criticism for a single moment. But he does radiate an atmosphere of unalloyed human sympathy, which Dr. Fosbroke, our psychiatrist member, only the other day said he wished that he might emulate. Old Ned has only to nod his kind bald head, surrounded now by his austerely close-clipped white hair, to elicit immediate confidence. I am aware of this myself. Indeed I am often surprised, later, on recalling things I have told Old Ned about Mrs. Horlick and our married daughter and our son's recent disastrous marriage. I have wondered sometimes whatever had induced me, not that I am worried for a moment about his discretion. He has never asked me a single question. Nevertheless, Old Ned plus even one Old-fashioned is often equal to an hour on the couch of a Vienna-trained analyst. The men's bar would not be the same place at all without Old Ned. It would cease to be a sanctum of the soul.

It is, of course, a truism that alcohol is apt to unleash loquacity, but there is more than this in the redolent atmosphere of the men's bar at Happy Knoll when, after a day on the links, or even the card room, Old Ned, behind that genial length of mahogany, offers you a glass. For one thing, you never can be sure how much will be in it. Some-

times I do suspect that the dear old rascal deliberately plays favorites and plies those who interest him most with more Happy Knoll spirits than he does the others. After all, can anyone — even you or I — enjoy everyone equally? And after all, must there not be long, dull periods in any bar like Happy Knoll where business, save for week ends and holidays, is seldom brisk until late afternoon? For instance, Old Ned, it would seem, has recently developed a great fondness for Mr. Bert Byles, a new member of ours from Foxrun Road, and I can hardly blame Old Ned for this partiality after his hours of polishing and breaking glasses in a completely silent room, with all his friendly instincts frustrated. Mr. Byles, it seems, is an unusually outgiving person with an active thirst for sympathy, and he is beset by extreme difficulties, both personal and financial. It always does a lot of good to speak your troubles and to have Old Ned nod silently, and I may say in passing that other men's bar patrons are interested in the troubles of Mr. Byles, too, because he suffers out loud more eloquently than anyone else. Besides, it is very hard, I have found, in any barroom anywhere, to avoid becoming deeply interested in another's domestic difficulties, since these always fall into the patterns that are in the nature of a common experience. But under the grave attention of Old Ned such disturbed confessions assume a new depth and a new value not unlike the program of a radio mediation hour.

As a small example of what I mean, it seems that Mrs. Byles is addicted to what one might term pursuit by telephone. Frequently Mr. Byles has been said to retreat to the bar weeping when he is being paged in other portions of the club, but when he sees Old Ned with a bottle of bitters in his hand he knows that all is well.

Under Old Ned's auspices the men's bar at Happy Knoll is what General MacArthur might rightly term a "privileged sanctuary" for all husbands suffering from telephonic persecution. When the bar telephone rings and Old Ned answers, you know that you are safe. His voice, which in his best years was hoarse and unmusical, now carries a conviction all its own. Even a Happy Knoll wife who knows that her husband is in the bar believes momentarily that he is not, when she hears Ned speak. It may be, as frequently happens, that she will call again five minutes later, but you are still safe be-

cause of Old Ned's magic. His negative is firmer on
the second call, carrying with it an undertone of
outraged dignity. Few wives except Mrs. Byles ever
call a third time.

It has occasionally struck me as odd that Old Ned
should have great difficulty in adding up his bar
checks, because he actually has a fine head for business combinations. Our fellow member H. J. Culbertson would be the first to agree with this statement. You may remember that some years ago H. J.
absorbed Pasqual Power in a rather spectacular
manner. The transaction, as H. J. himself confessed
to me later, had placed him under a very considerable nervous strain and, in seeking relaxation, he
adjourned to the bar at Happy Knoll.

Without H. J.'s ever knowing how it happened,
he found himself telling of the whole transaction to
Old Ned, including certain details which H. J.
frankly confesses he had never even told his lawyers. He still says that he is amazed and that Old
Ned might have a "half nelson" on him if Old Ned
should ever wish to use it. The truth was that Old
Ned understood every one of the details that H. J.
told him. It is a touching tribute to him that H. J.
has never been worried for a single moment. The

bar at Happy Knoll still is a privileged sanctuary.

It should be a source of pride to the club that an enormous amount of important business has been transacted in the bar. The stock of the P. W. Brakeweight Company moved to a new majority ownership right under Old Ned's nose, aided by a few Manhattans but mostly by Old Ned's benign exterior. Several of our best tax lawyers have advised their clients regarding some very interesting methods of business deduction in the bar. There is no doubt that the membership of Happy Knoll comprises one of the finest groups in the world, but even at Happy Knoll there are mysteries. There is a family whose name I won't mention living on Foxglove Lane that broke up almost overnight. Old Ned knows the reason. A certain home on Willowrun Path burned very suddenly two years ago. Old Ned can tell you whether or not this fire was entirely accidental. You have undoubtedly heard repercussions of a fist fight in the card room last winter. Old Ned could tell you the reasons and the details, blow by blow — if he could be induced to talk. But as someone said there, only the other day — after choking down a third of Old Ned's whisky sours that were mixed for some reason with ginger ale — nothing ever gets by Old Ned but nothing ever gets through him either.

I must assure you quite frankly, Albert, that I am not retailing hearsay gossip. I know these things about Old Ned because he told them to me yesterday and a good deal more besides. It seems that poor Old Ned is just as worried as you and I are by this new element that wants to do over the men's bar. Poor Old Ned, who does hear everything, has of course heard that a small clique wants a newer, defter barkeeper. Naturally this makes him deeply disturbed, I might even say upset, and never in the years I have known him have I heard him talk as freely as he has in the last few days. In fact, he put his own case very eloquently to me only the other evening.

"I am close friends with many lovely and very important members at Happy Knoll," he said. "I think if you was to speak to them about me, they would hate to see me leave."

Frankly, I echo those sentiments, and I am willing to bet a lot of the old crowd and even some of the new crowd will, too. Happy Knoll would not be the same place without Old Ned. His disappearance would give a lot of members, including myself, a very real attack of mental anguish. I do not mean that Old Ned would not be a true-blue Happy Knoller no matter where he might end up, but I know you will agree with me he had better stay right here. It is true that he is not improving. It might be well to have a younger man to mix the drinks, but let's keep Old Ned behind the bar.

Several of us are already circulating a petition to this effect, and you may be interested to know that Mr. H. J. Culbertson, Mr. Byles, five of our best corporation lawyers and one of our bank presidents have not only signed but are calling up their friends. In fact, the sentiment for keeping Old Ned is becoming a landslide. The subject will be discussed at the next meeting of the Board of Governors. I don't think there will be any difficulty, but it might be as well if you would write a confirming letter, since you have been around the bar a good deal yourself. All you need to say is: "Should auld acquaintance be forgot? Keep Old Ned."

Cordially yours,
ROGER HORLICK

CHAPTER VI

The Annual Dinner

A letter to Mr. Albert Magill, President Emeritus of the Happy Knoll Country Club, from Mr. Roger Horlick, member of the Board of Governors, regarding plans for the Annual Dinner.

DEAR ALBERT:

When you see the date on this letter, you can doubtless guess why I am writing you. Three weeks from tomorrow evening the Happy Knoll Country Club will hold its Annual Dinner. I suppose it has been given this title to differentiate it from other seasonal festivities which are beginning to project our manager, Mr. Bedard, into serious psychosomatic difficulties, besides threatening to give many members, including myself, symptoms of sclerosis of the liver. I refer specifically to the Midsummer Dinner, the Halloween Dinner, the Thanksgiving Eve Dinner, the Christmas Dinner, the St. Valentine Dinner, the Spring Dinner, the Greens Committee's Dinner, the Atherton Smythe Bridge Trophy Dinner, the Golf Widows' Dinner, the House Committee Dinner and the President's Dinner, not to mention weekly functions such as the Saturday Night Dinner Dance Dinners and the Maids' Night Out Dinners. No wonder that the breakage of glass and crockery is on a sharply rising annual curve. And no wonder, since a souvenir-collecting spirit seems prevalent among invited guests, that oyster forks, spoons and even soup ladles bearing the Happy Knoll name and crest must continually be replaced or that the restaurant deficit is rising. You may say that this deficit is counterbalanced by the increased bar receipts, and this well might be so, if the extra waiters would insist on a prompt signing of every bar check and if all signatures were identifiable. I am not impugning for a moment the honest intentions of the average Happy Knoll member. At the end of a hard evening they cannot help it if their handwriting undergoes a change. Then too, pencils invariably disappear in the midst of Happy Knoll dinners. Also, the waiters themselves grow forgetful. Mr. Bedard has made some strenuous efforts to prevent the ingestion of half-finished drinks in the pantry and kitchen and elsewhere, but he cannot be everywhere at once.

I am sorry to continue along these lines, but it is my unfortunate duty to be chairman this year of the Annual Dinner Committee. Its cost should presumably be covered by a fixed charge to each individual attending, but as you know very well, there comes a point of financial intolerance. After all, the Happy Knoll Annual Dinner is not a sounding board either for Mr. Adlai Stevenson or Mr. Averell Harriman, and no one will cheerfully pay $100 a plate. Thus it has, as you know, become a tradition that former members of the Dinner Committee each make a small contribution. Why else should certain persons have been chosen?

Yesterday, for your information, the committee met in the Pendleton Room. Some of the old guard, including Bill Jonas, were there, but not a few were strangers to me, mainly junior executives from that new development on Foxrun Road and, consequently, all were comfortably off. As a connecting link between us there was Bob Lawton, a conspicuous success in sales promotion. I don't know how well you know Bob Lawton, but I can safely say that he is a person of great enthusiasms and one who always takes over any meeting by offering what he calls constructive suggestions.

He immediately took control of this one by asking how could the Annual Dinner be made different? After all, Happy Knoll must not get calcified, must it? Very frankly, in Mr. Lawton's opinion, the Annual Dinner was delightful and many of the older members were lovable and indispensable, but it should not be what Mr. Lawton termed a horse-and-buggy dinner. Since we were speaking confidentially, it might be better, lovely though they were, to dream up some new speakers and new stories this year. Mr. Lawton had been to seven annual dinners, not having been in the club as long as some others, and nobody liked hearing a good story better than Mr. Lawton, even once or twice, but must one hear it indefinitely? For example, for the last seven years Mr. Hank Stevens — and this did not mean Mr. Lawton was not very fond of Hank — had told an identical story about two characters named Mike and Ike who had endeavored to enter a hansom cab outside of Delmonico's restaurant on Fifth Avenue simultaneously. They bumped heads, apologized, walked around the cab in opposite directions and again collided. This action with the speaker's words and gestures was admittedly convulsive, especially to older members, who always said that Hank was telling it better this year than he had for the last ten years. Then, too, the punch line was hilarious when Ike said in dialect, "Oi, oi, I now forget who I am; am I Ike or am I Mike?" But then, given time, didn't enough always become too much? Also, there was the sleeping car story customarily delivered by Mr. H. J. Culbertson about the elderly lady in lower 10 and the man in upper 10. After the train departed, the upper 10 passenger, a drummer, sat for a while in the gentlemen's washroom drinking from a bottle, and Mr. H. J. Culbertson invariably gave a splendid imitation of drinking from a bottle. In the course of time this character called to the porter in a bibulous manner and asked to be assisted to his upper berth, and the colloquy with the porter was sidesplitting if you'd heard it only once or twice, because Mr. H. J. Culbertson could change quickly from an intoxicated traveling salesman to a deep Negro dialect. Then when the man in upper 10 went to sleep and began to snore, this sequence, too, was excruciating because no one in the Happy Knoll Country Club could do a better snoring imitation than Mr. H. J. Culbertson. It was very amusing, too, when the old lady began to pound upon the berth above her, except that when Mr. H. J.

Culbertson arrived at this routine, he was apt to damage wineglasses and cups. And again, the punch line had true entertainment value: "It ain't no use, ma'am," the drummer said, "I seen you when you got in." It was an aisle-rolling story once or twice, but after seven years, could there not be a change?

Then there was Tom Gaspell and his guitar. Happy Knoll would not be the same without Tom, but still, Happy Knoll might get along without him occasionally. The Kipling poem "The Ladies" set to music, "I've Taken My Fun Where I've Found It," was undoubtedly nostalgic, but need it be sung always? And need the finale always be about the waitress who said to the drummer in the restaurant, "You would not dare insult me, sir, if Jack were only here"?

Well, Mr. Lawton said, he could go on; but briefly, his point was that all of this was good entertainment but timeworn, including the recitation by Mr. Godfrey Bledsoe of the Alfred Noyes poem, "The Highwayman." Frankly, a lot of younger Happy Knoll members had never seen a hansom cab except in a Sherlock Holmes illustration and thought a drummer was someone who worked in a jazz orchestra. No doubt Happy Knoll was a fine old club, but how about beaming the entertainment forward a little bit, say to pre-World War II? There were some pretty funny younger members, including Willie Atherton and Charlie Cromley, even if they had lived it up a bit at the Bledsoe coming-out party. Why not loosen things up and get the Annual Dinner out of its wheel chair and put it on roller skates?

Up to this point, Bob Lawton said (and he begged for our attention for just a moment longer because he had not as yet got to the real nub of his thinking), his criticism had been destructive. However, he did have some constructive suggestions and he wanted to toss off just a few of them. How would it be to loosen up the Happy Knoll Dinner by not having it a stag affair any longer? How about asking the Happy Knoll gals to be with their husbands this year? This startled us, didn't it? But after all, Happy Knoll gals were no longer like the gals in an Edith Wharton novel — not like that Edith Wharton gal named Lily Bart who got in wrong socially because she had a cup of tea alone in the apartment of a stuffed-shirt young man whose name Mr. Lawton was glad to say he had forgotten. Personally, he was pretty proud of Happy Knoll gals. They could tap-dance, jitterbug, play excellent golf and tennis, looked very lovely in Bermuda shorts and, generally speaking, could hold their liquor. Besides, they mostly made lovely wives and mothers. And to prove it, in the last year there were only 24 broken homes in the Happy Knoll membership — a ridiculously low percentage, judged nationally censuswise. Then why not admit that Happy Knoll gals were sophisticated people who could even stand that story about the hansom cab if necessary?

This was suggestion No. 1, but he did have some other ideas just off the top of his head. Instead of these set speeches, how about a rehearsed floor show derived from talent among the younger members? Charlie Cromley could do a lovely act with the saxophone, and the young Fosbroke girl, who had just finished her analysis, was the best blues singer that you ever heard, and never mind what people were saying about her and Art Beckett, the tennis pro, either. Then there was the young Whidden girl, who could shake out one of the prettiest hulas, grass skirt and all, that you could see this side of the Royal Hawaiian. Why not let some of this young talent take over? And he had a title for the program that just came out of his head, "Young People's Night at Old Happy Knoll." It didn't quite "sing" yet, but he could polish it up. Then if things were dull at points, why not hire one of those pro entertainers who did a drunken waiter act? Well, this was all he had to say — broadly speaking, a new streamlined sort of dinner with a good transfusion of youth and sex in it. He had just been talking off the top of his head, but he hoped that he had left some thoughts with us. If you wanted to put it in a single capsule, his message could be put in a single word — decalcify — and how about it?

There was a silence when Mr. Lawton had finished that obviously indicated a cleavage in the room, between the old and the new guard. I could think of what Marshal Ney said at Waterloo and also of the maxim, "Youth will be served," although I should only technically term Mr. Lawton a youth. I was glad that Bill Jonas made a rejoinder before anyone else had the opportunity. I understand that he was excellent in his time at addressing the Supreme Court, but I do not believe he was ever better in his prime. Though calcified, he said that he had listened with genuine attention and often with interest to Mr. Lawton's constructive suggestions.

Though senile, he loved to feel that he could still fall in with the thoughts of youth and, as Mr. Longfellow had once said (whom Mr. Lawton had perhaps read along with Mrs. Wharton), the thoughts of youth were long, long thoughts and so were Mr. Lawton's, though this was no criticism of their content. For a moment, superficially, he proposed that we might consider Mr. Lawton's suggestion of a professional drunken waiter. Since Happy Knoll was running at a deficit, why pay for an artificial drunken waiter when flocks of real ones would be present at the Annual Dinner — and at no additional cost? Admittedly this was a superficial criticism, but if you looked after the pennies, the dollars would take care of themselves. This axiom was not as strong as it might have been in his youth but, as a semiretired tax lawyer, he felt that it still occasionally had value.

Next, if Mr. Lawton would allow him, he might say that, being older, he was even more familiar than Mr. Lawton with the story of Mike and Ike and the hansom cab. He was sure also that he knew better than Mr. Lawton the story of the elderly lady and the drummer in upper 10, and he was an authority on Kipling's poems set to music; and if we

wished, although he hoped we didn't, he could recite "The Highwayman," by Mr. Alfred Noyes
with suitable gestures — but after all, would a saxophone act or a hula be any better? There was one
thing that Mr. Lawton was bound to learn eventually. In the end, any country club dinner was always calcified. Why did anyone ever attend such a
dinner except because of tradition? Why else did
one listen from youth onward to Bach? Why did
the Chinese attend for two thousand years their
stylized theater? Partly because of sloth but also because they did not like to be disturbed by new
thoughts and forms. Some day when Mr. Lawton
was older he would understand that there was a
routine about the Annual Dinner at Happy Knoll
as inevitable as a drama by Euripides. First, the formal greetings at the cocktail hour, the stylized bad-
inage, the gentle horseplay, the controlled shouting
across the table and, at last, the stories. It would be
a shock to any established member to have these different when his mind had been geared for decades
to performance rather than content. How might he
react at such a time if some member's young daughter triumphantly off an analyst's couch should sing
blues or if a strange girl should dance a hula? He

did not believe that he, or anyone else present, could happily adjust to any such sudden change.

Fortunately, as Mr. Jonas said, such a contingency would not be possible this year, at least, because, due to its constitution, membership at Happy Knoll was so far confined entirely to the male sex. This might be old-fashioned; he dared say it was. He would be the first to admit that Happy Knoll would be bankrupt were it not for the extraordinary participation of wives and daughters in its expanding facilities, including the ladies' bar, but in the end he wished to ask a pertinent question. Why was it that women went to Happy Knoll? Only because men started going there first. And why was it men first went to Happy Knoll? Only, he was afraid, to escape from domestic ties, stronger in America than in other parts of the world. It was odd, was it not, that in this streamlined age of Mr. Lawton's, men and women converged at Happy Knoll, one sex to pursue and the other to escape? It was confusing that their purposes should intermingle on the Saturday night dance floor, in the parking lot, upon the tennis court and even in mixed foursomes on the links. But still, there was that original purpose and that primary drive for exclusion, and it was still part of the spirit of Happy Knoll. In some way it had to be symbolized, and the Annual Dinner existed as this symbol. It had the segregated qualities that Lycurgus had once set forth in his constitution for ancient Sparta. The dinner was a bore, the speakers were all bores, but they were essential for the morale of Happy Knoll. Unlike Mr. Lawton, he had only two pertinent changes to suggest. Instead of the predinner Martinis being mixed at a ratio of four to one, he suggested a mixture of five to one, and also caviar to be paid for by previous committee members.

You will be glad to know that plans for the dinner have since continued without interruption. Hank Stevens will again tell his story of the hansom cab, H. J. Culbertson is already rehearsing his tale of the man in upper 10, Tom Gaspell will play "I've Taken My Fun Where I've Found It," "Gentlemen-Rankers" and "Odd Fellows Hall"; Mr. Bledsoe will recite "The Highwayman" by Mr. Alfred Noyes. However, there will be a bright addition to the program. As a final number, Mr. Bob Lawton has consented to do a five-minute inspirational piece entitled "What the Happy Knoll Country Club Means to Me." I wish you might be here to hear him, but since you are not, and as you may not have your checkbook handy, I am sending you a blank one on your bank.

Most sincerely,
ROGER HORLICK

CHAPTER VII

Hot Words

*Correspondence between Mr. Roger Hor-
lick of the Board of Governors of the Happy
Knoll Country Club and Mr. Albert Magill,
President Emeritus, regarding a Saturday afternoon incident in the men's bar.*

DEAR ALBERT:

I am writing to you today on behalf of the Board
of Governors of the Happy Knoll Country Club to
enlist your advice on a problem of discipline that
confronts us. You will probably have guessed already that I am referring to the physical collision
which occurred between two of our members, Mr.
Oscar J. Beight and Mr. George Plankton, in the
men's bar last Saturday at the end of a card-playing
afternoon. Bridge, as you have often said, more frequently than not arouses ill feelings when the players begin reviewing intonations of the bidding at
the bar. It is true from what we gather that Mr.
Beight and Mr. Plankton had been partners in a disastrous rubber, but their argument in the bar con-

[83]

cerned golf and seemingly ended on an ideological
note. I have learned that Mr. Beight, whom I have
never met personally, customarily refers to himself
as a Jeffersonian Fair Dealer. Whereas George
Plankton, as we all know, is the president of the
Plankton Bushing and Wire Company and has just
returned from Washington where he attended some
sort of Senate investigation. This will explain the existence of strained nerves and tension, but I know
what you are going to say.

You are going to say, why should the Happy
Knoll Board of Governors project itself into an im-
mature dispute? These are times, you are going to
say, of high spirits and frayed patiences, especially
with the hesitation that is now occurring in the
stock market. You will also add that there have
been other crises at Happy Knoll, in the men's bar
and elsewhere, that have been solved without resort
to official action. We have not yet forgotten at one
of the Saturday dances only last summer that the
Jeffers boy bit the Henty boy's ear, and then of
course there was the scratching in the ladies' locker
room after the August Four Ball. You might very
well say that forgive and forget has ever been a
motto at Happy Knoll.

I only hope we can apply it in the present case, and as a move in that direction I have questioned a number of people who were in the bar last Saturday, including Old Ned, who says it was his fault, that he just did not get moving fast enough. Both the members, he says, were gentlemen to the end, but he also adds that boys will be boys and girls will be girls at the end of a rainy Saturday. I wish we could leave it all on this note, but unfortunately both Mr. Plankton and Mr. Beight have submitted letters of complaint. They have been asked to withdraw these letters and they have both refused. We hope very much that you will advise us in this matter and thus for your information I am sending you both the Beight and Plankton letters. As you might expect, they run to cross purposes, but each has its own appeal.

Sincerely,

ROGER HORLICK

Letter from Mr. Oscar J. Beight to the Board of Governors of the Happy Knoll Country Club.

GENTLEMEN:

I hope it is needless to say that I have learned with regret that a contretemps which occurred between

[85   ]

myself and a fellow member of the Happy Knoll Country Club, Mr. George Plankton, has already become common property in this community and is approaching the dimensions of scandal. Feeling myself in no wise to blame for this state of affairs and being a married man and the father of two small children, I am sending this letter as an explanation but not as an apology. I realize, of course, that Happy Knoll purports to be a democracy and may be so in certain respects, but in a democracy a divergence of opinion should be permitted without a resort to fisticuffs and abusive language. Though a comparatively recent member and one who is not known to any of you gentlemen, I maintain that I still have a right to a courteous expression of opinion in the bar of the Happy Knoll Country Club, or anywhere else, nor do I believe I am of a quarrelsome or contentious disposition.

It is said that my dispute with Mr. Plankton arose over a game of bridge. This is not the case, although Mr. Plankton and I met at the bridge table. Frankly, being a somewhat recent member, I have never joined in a Saturday bridge game at your club and should not have on this occasion if I had not returned home from Washington that morning to find that Mrs. Beight and the children had gone to spend the day with her mother. Consequently, I went to the club for a sandwich and later entered the card room by accident. I must say that I was treated cordially and Mr. Plankton asked if he had not seen me in Washington the day before. I answered that he had, in Committee Room 213, where I had gone on the invitation of the committee's lawyer. Mr. Plankton made some remark that it was not a committee hearing but a star-chamber procedure.

"They as good as put a midget on my knee," he said. "How would you like to play some bridge?"

I only go into these details to show that there was no hard feeling between myself and Mr. Plankton. On the contrary, I admired his sportsmanship. I regret we neither of us understood the other's bidding. As a result, we both lost more heavily than was necessary, but we neither of us reproached the other and eventually adjourned to the men's bar for a drink. I offered to purchase a drink for Mr. Plankton and he bought me one in return. Yet I must assure you that there was no overindulgence, although your barkeeper, to whom Mr. Plankton introduced me, a salty old character who said I must return there often, was perhaps somewhat overgenerous with his measuring.

"Aren't you new around here?" Mr. Plankton asked me.

I told him I'd only come to the neighborhood since the change in administration in Washington.

"You mean," Mr. Plankton asked me, "that you were in Government under the Truman Administration?"

I told him that I had been and that I considered Mr. Truman a modern Andrew Jackson.

"I don't agree with you," Mr. Plankton said, "but I will buy you another drink."

It seemed to me that this was an excellent means of passing off this situation and it seemed only fair to buy him another in return.

I merely go into these details to prove that our conversation was amiable, with a display of good will on both sides.

"I guess I saw you on the golf course last summer, didn't I?" Mr. Plankton said.

I told him that I played occasionally. Frankly, gentlemen, I am interested in golf in spite of the fact that it is a sport indulged in by individuals who are so far to the right politically that their chatter in the locker room has often made me uncomfortable.

"Didn't you find the caddie situation terrible?" Mr. Plankton asked. "It's been the worst I've ever known it. Somehow kids don't seem to enjoy caddying any more at Happy Knoll."

I told him that I have never hired a caddie on general principles but always keep a folding golf cart in back of my car.

"If there weren't any golf carts, there would be more caddies," Mr. Plankton said. "What's the matter with hiring a caddie?"

Since the conversation had been most friendly, there seemed to be no harm in expressing my opinion. Also several other members had gathered around us and were listening with friendly interest.

Frankly, gentlemen, I have long taken a deep interest in the democratic potentialities of the game of golf. The number of persons now being introduced to it by our rapidly spreading municipal golf courses is to me a constant delight. Also, intending no ill will to certain entrenched individuals, it has seemed to me on the whole fortunate that the financial affairs of many golf clubs are now at such a low ebb that their grounds are now open to passing motorists. The country club, if it is to survive, in my opinion, must be a democratic institution and this intermingling of golf enthusiasts from other places is fast becoming another Canterbury Tale. I wished, I said, that I were a Chaucer so that I could put it into verse.

I observed at this point that the group around us had grown larger and I was not offended when my views were not accepted with complete agreement by everyone.

"O.K.," Mr. Plankton said, "golf is becoming democratic, but why don't you like caddies?"

I saw no harm in telling him that caddies were to me an embarrassing archaic survival.

"You're right on that one," Mr. Plankton said. "They get more embarrassing every year. They sniffle and talk and whisper, and pretty soon they'll be organized by the CIO, but how do you keep your head down if you don't use a caddie?"

It may have been at this point, gentlemen, that I warmed unduly to the subject by saying that if I could not keep my head down without child labor and exploitation, I should rather keep it up. And then I added that the very name "caddie" is one of derision and servile contempt, since the term is ob-

viously derived, as I told Mr. Plankton, from the word "cad" meaning "low fellow." I did not care, I told him, to pay for the privilege of being administered to by a little cad, nor should any American boy since the Roosevelt revolution, in my opinion, be subjected to such a degradation.

My recollections from this point on are not as clear as they might be, due to the confused discussion that followed. Finally Mr. Plankton tapped me on the chest and shouted that I was a parlor pink and called me a "cadet." I told him that this was no time for name calling, and at this point Mr. Plankton gave me a push, repeating the word "cadet," and I was obliged to cling to him in order to maintain my balance. Nevertheless, it appears that we both must have lost our balance almost simultaneously in that we were both helped up from the floor, and nothing further eventuated, except that Mr. Plankton again repeated the word "cadet," which, if I am not mistaken, is a contemptuous expression of social inferiority.

This is the whole incident, gentlemen, told, I trust, without bias or rancor, though it is my opinnion that Mr. Plankton behaved with the arrogance of a right-wing industrialist, which of course he is.

In spite of his connection with the Plankton Bushing and Wire Company, I believe your committee should ask him to apologize to me. If you do not agree, I shall be obliged to tender you my resignation from the Happy Knoll Country Club.

I am, gentlemen,

Yours respectfully,

OSCAR BEIGHT

Letter from Mr. George Plankton to the Board of Governors of the Happy Knoll Country Club.

GENTLEMEN:

As the head of an industry that is obliged to deal constantly with the AFL–CIO and who has to submit himself to annual investigations in Washington, I am fully aware that we have reached what is known by enthusiasts as "the age of the common man," but I have never been compelled to face this fact at the Happy Knoll Country Club until last Saturday afternoon. Mark you, I am tolerant. I understand as well as any of you gentlemen the need for broadening our membership base, but is it nec-

essary to let in Robespierres and Citizen Genêts? If
this sort of thing continues, you will end by having
a guillotine on the first tee and, being an optimist,
I do not believe this is necessary in the immediate
future.

I am referring, as you doubtless realize, to the
scene last Saturday in the men's bar at the Happy
Knoll Club when a new member made an aggressive motion toward me which was more than a vio-
lent gesture and which I was compelled to counter
in self-defense. The man's name is Oscar Beight. I
must ask to have him disciplined.

At this point I believe you gentlemen will agree
with me when I state that I am known for my
good-natured and easygoing disposition. Yesterday
afternoon I was cordial and even tolerant of Mr.
Beight, although his bridge game is such that I lost
eighteen dollars as his partner in half an hour. In
spite of *excusable* irritation, I took him to the bar
and offered him a drink when the game was over.
It may be that Old Ned, behind the bar, who as we
all know enjoys testing the capacity of new members, filled Mr. Beight's glass overliberally, but he
did exactly the same with mine. The conversation
turned to golf and Mr. Beight denounced the sys-

tem of caddying, calling it child labor and an insult to social conscience. I listened courteously while Mr. Beight bought me another drink, which again was poured by Old Ned. At the fourth drink, which I admit may have been overliberal, Mr. Beight said that the name "caddie" was a menial and insulting word, being derived from the word "cad." I told him in a quiet and courteous way that he was mistaken, "caddie" is the Scotch pronunciation of the French word *cadet*, brought to Scotland from France by the court of Mary Queen of Scots, meaning "little nobleman." For some reason Mr. Beight became incensed and said he refused to be insulted by being called a "cadet" or a "little nobleman" and he ended by calling me a "tory." At this point he gesticulated so violently that I was obliged to move backward and we both fell to the floor.

I conclude this letter by saying that if Mr. Beight will not apologize to me personally I shall resign as a member of the Happy Knoll Country Club. Incidentally, the Hard Hollow Country Club has invited me several times to become a member.

Respectfully yours,
GEORGE PLANKTON

Life at Happy Knoll

Letter to Mr. Roger Horlick of the Board of Governors at the Happy Knoll Country Club, from Mr. Albert Magill, President Emeritus.

DEAR ROGER:

The letters you have sent me have done much to relieve my mind. You know well how rumor surrounds such an episode as occurred at the men's bar last Saturday. I had heard that Mr. Beight, with whom I am not acquainted, had admitted to being a Communist card-holder and had threatened to organize our caddies into a labor union. I had also heard that Mr. Plankton struck Mr. Beight when Mr. Beight called him a cad. I had also heard that Mr. Beight had thrown Mr. Plankton through the bay window of the bar.

Thus the facts as you present them are reassuring. The difficulty between the gentlemen arose merely over terminology. If they are confronted with each other and the matter explained to them I am sure the difficulty will be over. All that is necessary is to say that if one resigns, both must. This ultimatum always settles these difficulties.

However, I cannot avoid the feeling that the real troublemaker in this scene would appear to have

been Old Ned, whose sense of humor has been growing recently. I suggest that he be spoken to firmly
and next summer be put in the men's locker room,

"old" Ned

an action which will be welcomed by various ele-
ments at Happy Knoll.

Hoping that this solution will appeal to you and
that you will not have to bother me again with such
minor problems, I remain

Very sincerely yours,
ALBERT MAGILL

CHAPTER VIII

Are Shorts Too Short
at Happy Knoll?

Letter to Mr. Albert Magill, President
Emeritus of the Happy Knoll Country Club,
from Mr. Roger Horlick, member of the
Board of Governors.

DEAR ALBERT:

At the last meeting of the Board of Governors a step was taken of which we all agreed you should be informed. We have finally drafted a letter regarding costumes to be worn by the club membership, particularly our younger ladies, this coming summer on all parts of the club property except the swimming pool and the adjoining area that includes the iron tables and the colored umbrellas. As you will doubtless agree from our experience last summer, it is impossible to control what people of either sex wear at the swimming pool except to state

in a general way that the Happy Knoll Country Club is not yet a nudist colony.

Our discussion, therefore, only concerned the general drift of bathing costumes into the dining room, the lounge, the mixed bar, the card room and even into the Pendleton Room; and this topic led naturally to the whole subject of shorts on both men and women inside and outside the clubhouse. There was a general agreement that something should be initiated this year regarding undue exposure, but there was a wide difference as to exactly what should be said by a governing board. In fact, the discussion became so heated that Mr. Bob Lawton, our new board member whom I do not believe you know, made what was to me a unique suggestion based on his experience as the executive of a large advertising agency.

It was Mr. Lawton's thought that there should be a sampling of public opinion among the club membership along the lines practiced by Dr. George Gallup in his Princeton statistical laboratory. Dismissing the remark of someone that Dr. Gallup had been wrong regarding the 1948 presidential election, Mr. Lawton advanced the opinion that Dr. Gallup had been right about everything else and that he had been virtually right about the 1948 presidential election, too, percentagewise. Mr. Lawton pointed out to us that in the "shop," as he calls his New York place of business, they use Dr. Gallup's prognostications almost constantly. Only the other day, he told us, their merchandise counseling service was undecided whether or not to advise a client to put a new-type diagonally stretching girdle into quantity production. A quick cross-sectional sampling was made of the three most reliable cities in the United States according to the Gallup rating. The question put up by the trained investigators was a very simple one: If you had the money to buy a girdle with a diagonal rather than a lateral stretch, would you buy it? The answers were very illuminating, according to the merchandise counseling at the "shop": yes, 21 per cent; no, 67 per cent; undecided, 2 per cent; don't understand, 10 per cent. As a result of this sampling of public opinion the client, the Safeside Stretch Company, will not put its new product into production at least for the present. It was Mr. Lawton's belief that it would not be necessary to consult the Gallup Institute directly regarding Happy Knoll. There was no reason why the Board of Governors should not sit right down now and dream up a question that would be a fair sampling of membership opinion. Just thinking off the top of his head, it was Mr. Lawton's idea that the same question should be sent to men and women alike in the membership, since boys and girls, as Mr. Lawton put it, had a common interest in shorts. In fact, right now, just off the top of his head, Mr. Lawton had a pretty good sampling question that we might at least kick around for a while. How would it be if a postcard were to be sent out to the membership with the following question: How short should shorts be at Happy Knoll? 1) knee-length Bermuda? 2) three inches above the knee? 3) six inches? 4) straight or curved? 5) loose, tight or medium? After each of these subheadings there should be a check list: yes, no, undecided, don't understand. This, in Mr. Lawton's opinion, would pretty well cover what he termed "the whole picture," and once the samplings were made and the results published, no one could have a reasonable kick about subsequent democratic regulations, and there should be no exceptions just because one gal's leg, as he put it, was more shapely than another's at Happy Knoll.

As often happens after Bob Lawton makes suggestions at our meetings, there was a profound and thoughtful silence.

Admitting that the idea had its angles of merit, there was also something wrong about it. I am delighted to say that Hank Stevens put his finger on the difficulty.

"And just exactly how do you think we would look as an executive body," he said, "if we were to send out an inquiry on how short women should wear their shorts? We ought to decide on the correct length here and now on the basis of our own experience."

What would they say at the Hard Hollow Country Club, he inquired, if we sent out any such round-robin letter, Dr. Gallup or no Dr. Gallup?

There was another silence, and then Tom Gaspell made what I still think is an interesting observation. There was no trouble about shorts being too short at Hard Hollow, he said, because most of the women there had given up trying to attract men. Besides, women at Hard Hollow had to play golf in long slacks whether they liked it or not because of the mosquitoes. There was another longer pause. Obviously everyone must have recalled the shorts that Mrs. Gaspell had worn last season, which were

[103]

so arranged that when she wore her cashmere coat it did not seem that she had on any shorts at all. Fortunately Mr. Gaspell continued with another thought. He said that he did not care what sort of shorts the women wore as long as they looked all right in them, and that was what Mrs. Gaspell always said, also. Some women looked all right in shorts and others looked perfectly terrible. It was not the fault of the shorts, but the fault of the individual who fitted herself inside them. Why not get a Gallup poll about the shape of individuals?

It was here that Bill Jonas made a suggestion. You can always count on Bill Jonas to have a good idea.

"Why not pass a regulation," he said, "to have shorts cut to fit individuals instead of forcing individuals into previously cut shorts?"

Bob Lawton said that this gave him a further thought.

"Why not," he said, "add another question to the public opinion poll: Are your shorts readymade or tailormade?"

"It doesn't seem to me we're getting anywhere with this discussion," Bill Jonas said. "We seem to be talking only about women's shorts."

At this point Hank Stevens made a further contribution. "Men wearing shorts," he said, "especially around a country club, pose another problem."

"I don't see how the hell they do," Bill Jonas said.

"Don't men and women wear shorts for basically the same reason?"

"That is a very interesting question," Bob Lawton said, "from a merchandising angle. The other day at the 'shop' we collated a number of surveys which we had made recently, apparelwise. They revealed discrepancies in various people's motives for selecting certain types of clothing."

"Don't men and women both wear shorts in order to keep cool?" Bill Jonas asked.

This, as you may imagine, evoked a further discussion. If women at the Happy Knoll Country Club wished to be cool, why was it that some of them did not wear shorts at all? You could take the Gladsbys' daughter, who last summer wore skin-tight silk breeches in the pattern of a leopard skin. Then there was the Hopewell girl, who wore fireman's-red trousers, one leg longer than the other, with slits halfway to the thigh and with small bells along the sides. Were these garments selected for coolness? Then there were the tight silk shorts that Mrs. Gladstone Blithe had purchased after her stay in Reno, to look like South Sea tapa, which created more attention than the red trousers.

There has, as someone pointed out at the meeting, been a considerable change in the last few decades in attitude toward costume. The poem of Suckling's about her feet peeping out from beneath her petticoat like little mice would now be incomprehensible at Happy Knoll on an August afternoon. In fact, to the best of my recollection ankles have never been mentioned at Happy Knoll since the start of World War II, and the musical comedy *Ankles Aweigh* was not so successful as *South Pacific*, perhaps because of its timid title. That other nautical expression, "Show a leg," would be more fitting for a summer day at Happy Knoll. I am sorry you were not with us to join in this discussion.

The sense of the meeting, as has been said previously, was that some people look well in shorts and some do not; but should one penalize people who do not look well merely because others do? You have to admit, Albert, that this is a real problem and one which may cause much ill feeling in unexpected quarters. I am afraid our discussion was not helped by a further suggestion of Bob Lawton's. His final one was to have a shorts-popularity contest directly before the Fourth of July Ball. Everyone who had been wearing shorts at Happy Knoll would be required to join the contest, each paying an entrance fee which would be applied to the cost of the new tennis court. A prize would be given, as a gag, for the shorts most likely to succeed.

I can only add that the meeting had obviously

gone far enough. At the end the following draft for a form letter was prepared to be sent to the membership by the Board of Governors:

DEAR FELLOW MEMBER:

It is not the wish of the Board of Governors to set clothing styles or fashions at the Happy Knoll Country Club. However, it has been noted that due to the constant change of summer fashions members may unwittingly appear dressed in a more bizarre manner than they intended. Therefore, solely to protect members from themselves, the following regulation will be put in force this summer at Happy Knoll:

Members and visitors at the Happy Knoll Country Club will be fully dressed at all times when inside the building. This regulation does not apply to the mixed bar, the terrace or the swimming pool.

— BY ORDER OF THE BOARD OF GOVERNORS

It seems a pity so much time was consumed in composing this letter, which I hope you agree completely covers the entire situation.

Please let us know if you think it does not.

Always sincerely,
ROGER HORLICK

CHAPTER IX

Are Women People at Happy Knoll?

A letter to Mr. William Jonas, chairman of the Board of Governors of the Happy Knoll Country Club, from Mrs. I. J. Felton, wife of Mr. I. J. Felton, a member of the Happy Knoll Country Club.

MY DEAR MR. JONAS:

Although I do not know you personally, I am sending you this letter because I believe you to be chairman of the Board of Governors of the Happy Knoll Country Club. At least, when my husband pointed you out to me, he told me that you were, but then, Ingram is apt to be very inaccurate, on Saturday afternoons. However, you were on the 18th green, which is not far from the terrace where women are allowed to buy drinks and, judging from your restrained dress and manner, you may very well be what Ingram said you are. Also I feel impelled to write to someone in authority instead of entrusting my complaints to Ingram, who is never accurate when carrying messages even to a drug-store.

Briefly, I am writing to complain regarding the general situation existing in the ladies' locker room at the Happy Knoll Country Club — a region with which I cannot believe you are in the least familiar, and there are unfortunately no women as yet on any Happy Knoll governing board. Happy Knoll is, as Ingram reiterates, whenever I criticize the place, a Man's World, and for once I believe he is right, which leads me to ask a question before I lodge my series of just complaints.

Are women people?

Although Ingram tells me that before you retired you were a leading lawyer in New York City and you served on civic committees with women prominent in society and professional life, I fear I can foretell your answer. This makes no difference, since I know the correct one, from my experience as president of the Parent-Teacher Association, of the local League of Women Voters, and as a former president of the State Association of Garden Clubs. My answer is that in all the wide workaday world of give and take, including the United Nations and Bryn Mawr College, my alma mater, women are people — *but not at the Happy Knoll Country Club*. I know the reason for this as well as you, Mr. Jonas. Men, I have observed, are afraid of women who have ideas which are even remotely abstract. Society, as it was founded in my youth, and even more so in yours, Mr. Jonas, judging from my glimpse of you, was founded on that fear. Men retreated then to such places as the Happy Knoll Country Club and, I regret, continue this outmoded practice, except for a growing number of enlightened young couples who share the burdens of marriage equally, including dishwashing and the care and entertainment of infants. I am happy to perceive that a hint of this spirit is now infiltrating Happy Knoll by way of the younger set, but admittedly it is still far from prevalent. Yet women do have rights, Mr. Jonas, even at your so-called country club, in spite of their lacking democratic representation save on the garden and decorating committees. And what, briefly, would you do without us? Have you ever pondered that question, Mr. Jonas?

By statistics, more women than men use your tennis courts. Half the greens fees on the golf course are paid by women. Women pay more than half of

the teaching fees collected by your professional,
Mr. Muldoon; especially, if I may say so, Mrs.
Meadows of the younger golfing set, who whenever
I seek an hour's instruction is taking a playing les-
son with Mr. Muldoon at some distant part of the
course. This, you may say, is neither here nor there,
but such facts reinforce my point that women more
than share the financial burdens of Happy Knoll.
The restaurant would perish without the patronage
of Happy Knoll wives and their guests, and at long
last you have displayed, though reluctantly, the
acumen to admit women to the new bar. But in
spite of the desegregation triumphs in the South we
are still second-class citizens in your organization.

What is the reason for this, Mr. Jonas? Is it because my sex is socially unattractive as a group? Is
it because women are not supposed to compete with
men in outdoor sports? Physiologists are now prov-
ing that women are more robust than men, out-
doors and indoors, Mr. Jonas. They have greater
qualities of character and endurance, can bear pain
with a stoicism of which a male is incapable — and
what man has ever borne a baby? Besides, the statis-
ticians have now proved that a woman's life span
is years longer, on the average, than that of the

comparable male — and this is itself a factor in women's rights at Happy Knoll that has been overlooked by your governing board. Actually, the sums expended by Happy Knoll widows do more toward supporting the club than the low scale of dues extended your younger male members, though admittedly these individuals eventually may marry and thus finally contribute to the widow backlog. I therefore ask you again: Are women people? Are they or are they not useful to you at Happy Knoll? Or should they be confined in their suburban homes with their knitting, where a great many men, including yourself, I am afraid, Mr. Jonas, appear to desire them?

I shall grant, as you will doubtless state in rebuttal, that you have made concessions to women and their wants at Happy Knoll. You have instituted the Saturday-night dances, though more for your amusement, I fear, than ours, judging from the frequent rumors of near seductions which are said to take place in parked cars and in the improperly lighted shrubbery behind the tennis courts. It is true, also, that you have enlarged the restaurant and, because of pressure brought to bear by wives of bankers and others in higher financial brackets than those enjoyed by Mr. Felton and myself, have finally discharged your wretched cook, who was able only to prepare fried chicken and fattening French-fried potatoes. Nevertheless, the dining room, and indeed the lounge, though recently redecorated in a vulgar manner under the auspices of a member (who I have heard pocketed her 33⅓ per cent commission without a by-your-leave), still reeks of deep fat. It is true also that you have opened what you call, unoriginally, the *mixed* cardroom, as well as the *mixed* bar, where a woman may be seen without her husband with only a modicum of comment as long as she is not seen with someone else's, however platonic their relationship.

I do admit that such innovations, wrested from reluctant managements after struggles comparable to India's before she received her independence, do, in fact, exist. But what of other areas? What of the men's bar, where a generation of wives have met rebuff or insult, depending upon the time of day, when they have attempted to inquire of their husbands' whereabouts? What of that frightful chamber of horrors known as the Pendleton Room, that has housed its grotesque collection of trophies won by Happy Knoll males since the inception of the

Pendleton Room

club, and open only to Happy Knoll women on the occasion of the New Year's eggnog? Golf, bridge and tennis trophies won by Happy Knoll women's teams are still in a state of segregation, standing inconspicuously in a glass case in the entrance hall beside the ladies' powder room. I shall conclude merely by confining myself to the men's locker room, of which Mr. Felton gives me many glowing accounts. Why is it that twenty thousand dollars was voted last year for innovations in the men's room and only three hundred and fifty dollars for the ladies'? *Are women people?*

The dressing cubicles in the men's locker room, Ingram informs me, are made of fumed oak and resemble choir stalls. Near these stalls is a table containing assortments of baby powders, foot ease and hair ointments. These latter are necessary but, judging from the thinning hair at Happy Knoll, they have, to date, proved ineffective. Also, Ingram tells me, this commodious room has a new crimson carpet, and the benches in front of the modern noiseless lockers are lined with foam rubber. There are also occasional armchairs, each with its table for beverages, and a sideboard with real glasses and no paper cups. The shower baths, Ingram tells me, are beautiful, and my husband always uses restrained enthusiasm. There is some sort of composition on the floor, and he states that it is so effective that one can step on a cake of soap and still maintain one's balance, and a new appliance which prevents one's scalding oneself to death. There is also a cabinet for electrically warmed bath towels. I have sometimes thought that Ingram, when describing these innovations, has been "pulling my leg," but I doubt this because he is customarily factual and devoid of humor.

Believe me, I do not mean to denigrate the men's locker room, Mr. Jonas, but if it seems to arouse in me a spirit of wishful thinking, I must ask you to consider the women's locker room. Before entering this space, for your information, Mr. Jonas, one passes through a lobby or vestibule known among certain members of the club — I am sure I don't know why — as the ladies' rest room. No one could wish to rest there. This dingy cubicle is furnished with broken chairs and tables, discarded from happier parts of the premises. I only mention this because among the articles that have finally come to rest in this haven is a broken-backed tome entitled *Happy Days at Happy Knoll* — *1906.*

Having had the curiosity to peruse this item, I have learned that the wing of the club which shelters this annex was the original small building from which the rest of Happy Knoll has sprung. In those days the ladies' locker room was the men's locker room, a place where shoes were changed and in which two shower baths — something of an innovation in 1906 — were installed. These were, and still are, operated by strings. In case you do not know it, this retreat has undergone no appreciable change except for successive coats of beige paint. Even the bulbs of the light fixtures which hang by frayed wires from the ceiling date back, I really think, to the inception of Mr. Edison's incandescent lamp.

There has been only one improvement, obviously thought up by some member on a forgotten committee who had been inspired by the sight of a chorus girls' dressing room in the motion pictures. A long glass-covered powder table with a series of mirrors has been installed against one of the blank walls as far as possible from any light, either natural or artificial. Years of lipstick decorate its surface, as do flocks of paper cups used by the younger Bermuda-shorts set. After all, women — especially the modern ones — can sometimes be as thirsty as men, Mr. Jonas. You may well ask if the place is never put in order. I should, on the whole, say it is not, because it is presided over by a so-called maid named Doris, an elderly woman whose chief interest is to see that nothing remains in the paper cups, especially after tournaments. Need I go on, Mr. Jonas?

I fear I have gone too far already, since I have so often been reminded (as I have mentioned before) that it is a Man's World at Happy Knoll. I suppose we should be grateful that we are allowed to play on the links at all. Of course we all understand that golf is a man's game and that naturally we should never play it on Saturdays and Sundays when men, who are the breadwinners of the American family, require the course for male rest and relaxation. If they are breadwinners, I should like to ask you parenthetically how it happens that 65 per cent of America's wealth is in the hands of women, and not men? Still, naturally, men should use the golf course and the Pendleton Room and the men's dining room and the men's bar and the men's veranda, because it is a Man's World.

Consequently please forgive this letter, but permit me only one more remark, simply because women are conventionally believed to have the last word. Old fogies like you may not realize it, Mr. Jonas, but times are changing. In other places than Happy Knoll women are gaining their rights and are maintaining them. I know the burst of male guffaws when the Hard Hollow Country Club is mentioned, Mr. Jonas, but I may tell you that it is a forward-looking place. There are two women on Hard Hollow's board of governors, and a woman is now in nomination as vice-president of Hard Hollow. This may either shock you or excite your risibility, but results are already evident. The ladies' locker room at Hard Hollow is being redesigned by an interior decorator closely connected with the New York Museum of Modern Art. No wonder that the gayer and more successful of our young married couples are trending toward Hard Hollow! The course is open to all on Saturdays and Sundays too, and, frankly, I myself have been approached, Mr. Jonas. A word to the wise is sufficient. Happy Knoll may be a Man's World, but never forget for an instant that there are women in it.

Very respectfully,

LYDIA P. FELTON

CHAPTER X

Caddie Crisis

A letter to Mr. Albert Magill, President Emeritus of the Happy Knoll Country Club, from Mr. Roger Horlick, member of the Board of Governors.

DEAR ALBERT:

I know what you are going to say when you receive this letter. You are going to say that you cannot constantly be called upon to bail out the Happy Knoll Country Club. You are going to add that during the past year there have been too many fiscal crises and contingencies. You are going to ask, as you do always, why it is that certain members of our group who can afford it better than you, invariably run out of ready cash whenever the hat is passed. You are also going to say that only last week you contributed generously toward a new set of dentures for Old Tim because his last ones were broken while on duty in the men's locker room when he was seized with a fit of laughter at a practical joke played by one of our many pranksters. Although you remarked at the time that it was hard for you to see how this could be called an employee's injury in line of duty, you also added that you would contribute to anything, however indirect, which might improve Old Tim's personal appearance. When holes were burned in the new Oriental rug in the Pendleton Room during the recent celebration of Benny Muldoon's victory in the Invitation Tournament, you contributed toward the repair bills, only making the obvious remark that it might be safer in the future not to have Oriental rugs in the Pendleton Room. When the rear porch of the clubhouse unexpectedly collapsed as the new deep-freeze unit, to which you also subscribed, was being moved across it to the kitchen, you only sent a rhetorical question with your check which was, If the club building is falling to pieces, why not let it?

You must not think that the Board of Governors, not to mention the whole Happy Knoll membership, is not deeply appreciative of both your generosity and your suggestions. In fact, we are acutely embarrassed that so many new contingencies have recently arisen. I know you will say, having gone this far with this communication, that I would not have extolled your generosity if something new and serious had not transpired, and in this case, as almost always, you are right.

I need not remind you of your benign and almost paternal interest in the caddie situation at Happy Knoll, which is only exceeded by that of the young advertising executive, Mr. Bob Lawton, who, I must have told you, should never have been made a member of the Board of Governors. Unfortunately, if I may say so, you both react toward our caddie problem as though you were demagogic politicians in a welfare state. Yet, though I have sometimes disagreed, I have never violently objected to your eleemosynary steps in this direction because I, too, have found many of the boys who have spent their adolescence on the links at Happy Knoll individually beguiling. I hope that you will be as shocked as we on the Board of Governors were when we learned from Benny Muldoon and from Pete, the caddie master, that the caddie house situation, in spite of all the palliatives you have attempted, is deteriorating as rapidly as the world situation. We stand, at Happy Knoll, like our own great country — thinking of the money that has been spent, reviewing our good-will missions and the panel discussions, and then wondering what under the sun has happened.

What, you may ask, *has* happened? Nothing that may not be inevitable in this changing world, but the news is, according to Pete and Benny Muldoon, who are both themselves in a state of deep unrest, that the caddies are leaving Happy Knoll for other places, and that, if this regressive movement is not very shortly checked, members will begin pulling golf carts at Happy Knoll.

I know very well how strongly you feel about this contingency and how often you have said that a boy carrying the bag and replacing divots, even though he is afflicted by hiccoughs, is an essential part of a golf match. When he has disappeared, you have often said, a human element and a human hazard has also left the game. We know how the specter of pulling a golf cart has always haunted you, and we know also that your aversion does not arise because of class distinction, but because of your innate fondness for the game. We know the extraordinary steps you have taken in order to avoid this danger. It was you who had plumbing, something which none of us quite frankly had ever thought of associating with caddies, added to the caddie house.

It was you, too, when this change was made, who defrayed from your own pocket the cost of a caddie room equipped with easy chairs, magazines and checkerboards. It is not your fault that the chairs are hardly ever used or the checkerboards, either, because the young men, when inside, are invariably on their knees shooting craps. It may disturb you, but also interest you, that a recent delegation from the Board of Governors to the caddie room discovered there a five-cent gambling machine contributed by Old Ned, who oversees its operation. In fact, we believe that this explains why Old Ned has been so anxious lately to convert nickels into dollar bills, and why all the tills at Happy Knoll are filled with only nickels. I do not like to use the word "racket" in connection with Old Ned — but then, perhaps the Happy Knoll Country Club is merely the Great World in microcosm. It further appeared, when our committee looked into the affairs at the caddie house, that certain of the young men have been selling packets of recently invented "non-anxiety pills" for nervous and unsteady players. This seemed preposterous until pills were discovered behind a pile of *National Geographic* magazines in your caddie rest room. When analyzed, they proved to be salt tablets; but young Tommy Bailey said that Old Ned was selling the tablets, and arranging for their distribution. Upon being informed of this story, both Benny Muldoon and Pete said that the Bailey boy had been reading too many comic books, and when we attempted to question the Bailey boy again, he had entirely disappeared.

Unfortunately, not your rest room, nor the gambling facilities, nor pill peddling, nor all combined, are any longer sufficient to keep caddies at Happy Knoll. It is true you envisaged the problem, and we all have faced the question of what could be done now that teen-agers can pick up eight or ten dollars for mowing a lawn. Our answer was to make life more glamorous for caddies; and I may say Benny and Pete have been doing their best to make Happy Knoll the cradle of the Hogans of tomorrow by giving useful golf advice. And Tuesday is Caddies' Day. It was Bob Lawton, I believe, who inaugurated the Caddies' Tournament, and the green Caddie Hat with H.K. embroidered on it; and Benny Muldoon himself has made personal calls on caddies' mothers to explain to them the high moral atmosphere of Happy Knoll and its golfers.

Why is it, you may ask, that these intelligent and expensive efforts have borne so little fruit? Some of the Golf Committee have begun blaming the increasing lack of caddie interest on television, and it may be that the American boy is becoming effeminate or beginning to tire of the game of golf — but frankly, I believe the caddie shortage can be explained in a single word, namely: competition. Frankly, Albert, there are too many golf courses in this area, and too few boys when the caddie potential is being cut by wage inflation and other forms of entertainment. Unfortunately, too, other country clubs have also thought of the devices for caddie happiness that have occurred to us here at Happy Knoll, and the Hard Hollow Country Club is a painful illustration. Hard Hollow caddie caps, we have discovered, not only have a handsome H.H. but an embroidered figure of an American eagle that Hard Hollow has spuriously adopted as an emblem. In some unexplained manner, Mr. Benton Follen, the only really big stockbroker in Hard Hollow, has discovered a lawyer who has convinced the Bureau of Internal Revenue that a caddie's recreation room is a boys' school and consequently tax exempt. This has enabled Mr. Follen to pour a huge portion of his paper profits into a building whose tiled showers and foam-rubber chairs make your effort at Happy Knoll meager; and I am sorry to say there is a Hard Hollow pinball concession which is somehow classed as charity. But what is still more disturbing is the growing aggressiveness of individual Hard Hollow members. It has been revealed by our investigation that an intensive canvassing of potential caddies' parents has been made, not by their professional, Jerry Scalponi, but actually by a members' committee. These individuals have not only verbally extolled the advantages of Hard Hollow, but have also made unfair and defamatory attacks on Happy Knoll. The rumor, believe it or not, is being spread that the Hard Hollow environment is more salubrious for boys than Happy Knoll — and to prove it, a transcript has been made of the golf language of certain Happy Knoll members, including, we have learned, your own. Old Ned and his pills have not come off unscathed, either, and several mothers were told by a Hard Hollow member, in front of the meat counter of an A & P store, that Benny Muldoon and Pete run crap games. It was also said in the A & P store that Jerry Scalponi is

more interested in teaching caddies golf and is a better instructor and was once an Eagle Scout.

I know that such subversions will infuriate you as much as they have the rest of us and we all dislike to have you disturbed while you are still waiting for the final report on your last medical checkup, but something must be done immediately. The immediacy, I regret, is all the greater because of an agreement which our fellow governor, Bob Lawton — who had no business to speak in behalf of the whole club membership — made with Mr. Conrad Richtover, who, as you know, is now the president of Hard Hollow. Unfortunately, the ideas of Mr. Lawton are frequently as unsound as they are dangerous, and his enthusiasm constantly outruns his intelligence. It appears that he and Mr. Richtover met one afternoon at a cocktail party somewhere on Foxrun Road, where Mr. Richtover stated, facetiously I hope, that the only reason any caddie ever worked at Happy Knoll was due to the preposterous tips given them by certain wealthy members. Naturally, Mr. Richtover said, I hope facetiously, caddies were drawn to Happy Knoll by the Jaguars, Cadillacs and Bentleys in the parking lot. It seems, according to the somewhat garbled account of Mr. Lawton, that he expressed indignation. Tipping, he said, was impossible for the upstanding American boys who came to Happy Knoll. In fact, he was sure that it did not exist and he was sure that all our Board of Governors would be glad to make a gentlemen's agreement with Hard Hollow that members of neither club should tip, however great should be the temptation. You will say, and I will agree with you, that anything said at a Foxrun cocktail party means nothing, but unfortunately Mr. Lawton brought up the question at the recent annual meeting, where it was voted on favorably with the help of our tennis, swimming, backgammon and bridge membership, and there it stands. It means that our last leverage to hold caddies at Happy Knoll has been pulled out from under us by, frankly, the lack of alcoholic capacity of one of our newer governors. Personally I had no idea how important the incentive motive was until the "No Tipping" regulation was suddenly put into practice. It may be a degrading institution, but effective. Without it, Albert, I am very much afraid that the golf cart is here unless immediate measures are taken.

You cannot say that we are not ready with an

answer. Some of Happy Knoll's best lawyers have been working on one all last week, and here it is. There will be no tipping but there will be what is known as a Revolving Incentive Fund for Deserving Caddies. This fund will be divided at the end of the season, according to merit, to pay for caddies' schoolbooks and other school expenses; and thus it is our hope, although no promise can be made as yet, that the Bureau of Internal Revenue will pass it as an effort as educational and as tax exempt as that of the caddies' room at Hard Hollow. When this plan goes into operation, as it must, a huge thermometer will be placed at the door of the golf shop showing the rising amount of dollars being subscribed for the Caddies' Revolving Incentive Fund. If this does not catch the interest of our local youth, we shall all be very much surprised. The moment the fund is created, each caddie will have a card with a point system to be signed by the member who employs him; one point for average work and three points for excellence — but there will also be demerits. These will be: talking, sniffling, coughing and sneezing, one demerit each; laughter, three; taking practice swings with the employer's clubs, four; and ten demerits for any caddie seen taking a full swing with a putter on any green. Think what this revolving incentive fund will mean. It will mean, frankly, that Happy Knoll, because of its financial position, should be able to outbid any effort of Hard Hollow in this direction, whether these contributions are tax exempt or not. It will mean far more skillful caddies as much pledged to do kind deeds as are Boy Scouts. It will mean dedicated boys and the pick of the market. Try to keep them away from Happy Knoll when there is a Revolving Incentive Fund for schoolbooks! Try to make their parents not send them, daily!

This idea, I may confess, is entirely my own and I can see you catching fire already. The secret of its success is of course the subscription of a large initial sum and I believe that you or I should start the ball rolling. It must, I am afraid, be something substantial, and I fear I cannot do what I should ordinarily because unfortunately the Government has found an error in my recent tax returns which will set me back for many months to come. But I am sure it is different with you, Albert. What we need is a thousand dollars as a starter, and we know you always lead the way, and don't forget that time is of the essence. Why not telegraph the money before you forget it, just as soon as you receive this letter?

With all our thanks in advance,

Most sincerely,

ROGER HORLICK

CHAPTER XI

Locker Room Trouble

Letter to Mr. Albert Magill, President Emeritus, from Mr. Roger Horlick, Board of Governors of the Happy Knoll Country Club.

DEAR ALBERT:

I have never known a golf season at the Happy Knoll Country Club when there have not been a number of complaints lodged before the Board of Governors regarding conditions in the men's locker room, and added to this, there are now complaints from the ladies' room as well. But the conditions in the men's locker room, I would say, are more social than physical. Unfortunately, the usual groups and juntas seem to be more at daggers drawn than usual and consequently it may be necessary to issue and enforce new regulations.

There are, as always, the drinking and the non-drinking groups, or if you wish to put it in another way, the shower-and-change and the simple shoe-changing clique. You would think that the shoe-changers, who pay as much for their lockers and who simply sit in front of them and take their spiked shoes off as rapidly as possible and then retire

Old Tim

to the men's bar, where they can discuss their golfing difficulties in comparative comfort, would not be a source of trouble. Old Tim — who, I must say, is getting forgetful and seems even worse this year than last — has only to take the shoe-changers' shoes, clean them and place them beneath their lockers. Then his work is done. If the shoes are mixed up — for instance, as occasionally happens, one of Mr. Bentley's crepe shoes is found beside Mr. Robinson's spike shoe in Mr. Lockforth's locker, and both of them are lefts — you can count on a feeling of good fellowship and cooperation deriving from a genuine affection for Old Tim to straighten things out. Up to now this has all ended with a good-natured joshing of Old Tim, which Tim has grown to depend upon and enjoy, but the shoe-changers are making genuine trouble this year at Happy Knoll. Furthermore it seems that the shower-and-change group has also been growing more aggressive. The locker benches are becoming more and more filled with moist towels, moist undergarments and loose ice cubes, so that shoe-changers find it difficult to remove their footwear. We had hoped, as you well remember, that the generous gift to the locker room by H. S. Fosbroke of an attractive alcove with dark oak dressing stalls — officially known as the Fosbroke Alcove, and now called, I regret to say, the Fosbroke Boudoir — would obviate this difficulty. The shoe-changers, we had hoped, would all use the Fosbroke Alcove, which is much nearer the men's bar and would thus be separated from the more vociferous showerers. It has not worked out this way. It seems that the shoe-changers prefer benches in front of their lockers, as always. They insist that they are paying a high price for the use of these and several have insisted that the showerers and dressers use the Fosbroke Alcove and that a table be placed there with ice and set-ups. It would be no trouble, this element says, for the showerers to bring their bottles and flasks to the table, no matter what their nudity.

Superficially, this would seem like a worthwhile suggestion and it has always been my opinion that the bringing of private bottles into the locker room should be discouraged, since this practice cuts into the bar receipts; but there has been great objection to this move. It seems that most of the opposition centers around Old Ned who, you know, has been removed from the men's bar to the locker room this season. It gives Ned great happiness to circulate with trays of ice and soda, this being an activity which keeps him in touch simultaneously with his old friends in the bar and with his new friends near the showers, and there is no doubt that Old Ned is once more beginning to make himself indispensable. In an older day, when only glasses were available, the Fosbroke contingent might have moved to the Alcove, but with the two newly installed water coolers, this action is no longer necessary because it is always possible, even if Old Ned forgets the ice and set-ups as he very often does, to bring a flask or bottle to the water cooler and use paper cups. Also, Mr. Benjamin Carrow, who, as you know, has been a locker-room habitué for many years, is against all change. He is, if I may use the word, a ringleader of the shower-and-change group, just as Mr. James A. Mosser is organizing the shoe-changers. Recently both these members of Happy Knoll have written communications to the Board of Governors, which throws this controversy fully into focus, and I am sending you copies for your information and guidance.

Sincerely,

Roger Horlick

Letter from Mr. James A. Mosser to the Board of Governors of the Happy Knoll Country Club.

GENTLEMEN:

By way of introduction I beg to state that for the last twenty-two years I have been both an active and an appreciative member of the Happy Knoll Country Club. This longish period of membership dates from my first arrival in this community when I purchased for Mrs. Mosser, then but recently a bride, our present home on Wedgewood Lane directly after I was made a junior partner in the New York law firm of Caulkins, Bryan and Russell of which there now seems a prospect that I may become a senior partner if I can keep my health and memory together for another decade. It was for this purpose that I first joined the Happy Knoll Country Club and why, in spite of certain difficulties and grievances, I have persisted, often against Mrs. Mosser's advice, in retaining my membership. I have always been a believer in that old motto — and I believe my Latin is correct — MENS SANA IN CORPORE SANO. After the daily exigencies of a law firm in downtown New York, I have found that relaxation is necessary. Because of our Northern climate and the fact that Mrs. Mosser does not enjoy a winter golfing vacation, bridge is my hobby until the grass grows green upon the course at Happy Knoll. When this fortunate event arrives, Mrs. Mosser notwithstanding, I am able to counterbalance cares of the office by resorting to the still greater worries of golf.

Frankly, in spite of the tutorial money which I have paid to our professional, Mr. Muldoon, I cannot see that my game has improved perceptibly over the decades; but this, honestly, is not the point. The point is that I still hope it may improve, and therefore I play at the Happy Knoll Country Club on two weekday afternoons and on Saturday and Sunday mornings invariably, whether Mrs. Mosser may approve of it or not. For twenty-two years I have rented locker number 67 which stands nearest the aisle of Alcove G. I have never dominated this area. I have made but little noise. I have watched the personnel around me during my locker room life undergo considerable change. I am sorry to say that in recent years the change is growing more rapid and is declining toward the worse.

Each year more members appear to consider the alcoves between the steel lockers not as a dressing space for which they were intended, but rather as informal lounging rooms in which they can sit indefinitely in a semidraped condition, retailing loud anecdotes of their last eighteen holes or settling the interminable details of their complicated gambling debts. This tendency has immeasurably increased since Old Ned has been moved to the locker room from the bar to assist Tim, the regular attendant. I do not mean to imply that Tim does not need assistance. On the contrary, the increasing noise in the locker room throws him in a state of greater, if possible, than normal confusion; but the addition of Ned only makes confusion worse confounded because both Ned and Tim are so naturally gregarious that all they do is to stand listening and often joining in the conversation. The latter is easy for, though I have never fallen a victim to the charm of these two senile and incompetent employees, they are individually popular among the more heavy drinking groups.

I am the last person, I hope, to object to conviviality, but I do object to sodden bath towels, to paper cups and odd shoes and garments being strewn everywhere for weeks on end. During this season I have never seen Old Tim once pick up any of these articles. Indeed the only time I have seen him bend over was to grab for an abandoned fifty-cent piece, and to my amazement his reflexes were quicker than those of Old Ned. It may be that my instinctive liking for order makes me somewhat of a "stickler," but still I should be glad to put up with everything except for the occasions when I cannot get to my locker or open it because of the large number of moist individuals who loll in front of it and who actually seem to resent my intrusion.

I shall not name names or criticize any one member of Happy Knoll, but I will say this — that the sight of a middle-aged Happy Knoll member in the nude grows less aesthetic to me year by year. Balanced diet, I am convinced, does not interest many. At any rate, their physical bulk is continually between me and my shoes when I am able to find the latter. There used to be a time when persons would hear if I said "Excuse me," but now under the ministrations of Old Ned they are too preoccupied to hear or to move in any direction. In fact, I frequently feel as though I were among bodies falling into hell as depicted on the bas-reliefs of a medieval cathedral. Is this sort of thing sport, gentlemen? Is this for what Happy Knoll was intended?

These questions, I admit, are purely rhetorical. I have been told again and again that if I don't want a shower bath and a drink I should change my shoes in the Fosbroke Alcove, but how am I to do so?

Would Old Tim ever find my shoes if I left them there? Would he ever return them to my locker? The answer is, he would not. The only way to keep clothing and equipment safe at Happy Knoll is to put them firmly under lock and key, as are mine in locker 67. I am sorry to spoil the fun in front of locker 67, but I must get to it sometimes and it is not my fault that a certain Happy Knoll member collided with my key while it was in the lock and scratched his torso severely while demonstrating the follow-through he made on the difficult 10th. If there has been any complaint to the Board of Governors regarding this incident, I, too, must complain that there are other danger factors in the locker room besides keys. Only the day before yesterday, when arriving from the links, I stepped upon a number of ice cubes that had been accidentally dropped in the corridor by Old Ned. These became impaled upon my golfing spikes so that I slid a considerable distance, finally lost my balance and fell. This accident only caused our club nudists merriment instead of concern. In fact, Old Ned was too convulsed to be able to help me up and the injuries I suffered are today more serious than any key scratch.

Locker Room Trouble

This letter, gentlemen, is not a complaint; rather it is an invitation. Why does not your committee drop into the locker room at six o'clock some afternoon, or even at seven or eight, and hear some poorly told off-color stories, see some horrible physiques and slip on some ice yourselves? If you did, perhaps you would agree with me that any change, however insignificant, would be for the better.

Respectfully yours,
JAMES A. MOSSER

Letter from Mr. Benjamin Carrow to the Board of Governors of the Happy Knoll Country Club.

GENTLEMEN:

I do not like to indulge in personalities, especially as concerns members of so fine a country club as Happy Knoll, but maybe in this case I should, since I understand that Mr. James A. Mosser — who rents locker 67 in good old Alcove C — is writing you a complaint about what he calls "disorders" in the locker room. It gives me pleasure to state that neither I nor any of the gang have anything against this Mosser character personally — only he is a fussy, skinny old guy, like so many of these lawyers who argue over income taxes and never have any clean fun and lose all their sense of humor, if they were ever born with any. None of the gang has anything against him —we are only sorry he doesn't want to fit in with the group; and believe me, we have one of the swellest crowds in the locker room this summer that you gentlemen have ever seen — a whole lot too swell for any sorehead to go and ruin. Come to think of it, I have a right to be just as sore at Mosser as Mosser is at any of the gang. I ripped myself clean across the back last week because he left his key jutting out of his locker in Alcove C, an injury which made me lose my first match in the Four Ball. Nevertheless, I don't complain, even though Muldoon himself assured me I would have won if I had gone through the ball instead of wincing on impact, from the pain the scar gave me. *C'est la guerre* has always been my motto, if you will excuse my French. Neither I nor any of the gang has any gripes about Mosser. He is the one who is public griper No. 1, and his reason seems to me mighty trivial. Frankly, gentlemen, all it was: he stepped with his spiked shoes on some ice cubes that had fallen in the alley outside of Alcove C and then did just a simple pratfall.

It may have been the fault of our crowd that we laughed, as did Old Ned and Old Tim who were present at the time, hustling a few bourbons on the rocks. But what were we to do instead? Cry? And who can avoid laughing at those things? Remember the old vaudeville days? I still think a good bump on the rear furnishes the best sure-fire entertainment in the world. Anyway, he did not hurt himself, or if he did, it is only because he eats too much wheat germ and too much saccharine in his coffee and nothing else. Anyway the ice cubes were definitely not, as he intimated, put there for him to step upon, on purpose. The locker room gang may play jokes like that on ourselves, but never on outsiders. Why, frequently ice cubes get slithering around the locker room by accident, and twice on leaving the showers to get back to the bourbon in good old Alcove C I have stepped on them myself, barefoot. And in this connection, let me tell you, just for the laugh, the good line Old Ned got off the last time I did so. He said, It isn't everybody who is able to slide on ice in summer. Honestly, gentlemen, you cannot beat Old Ned. He is a jewel, and all the gang would be glad to die for him. You never did a wiser thing than move him from the bar, where his talents were wasted serving the quarrelsome stuffed shirts who seem to congregate in that place.

Anyway, this letter is not intended only to explain that you mustn't mind anything that Mosser says about what he calls "conditions" in the locker room. This epistle also comes from the whole gang to convey to you gentlemen our congratulations. The Happy Knoll locker room is, in my opinion, the finest locker room I have ever seen anywhere — and I've seen plenty in my day, beginning at Princeton where I used to do the 100-yard dash (I've put on weight since then). There is, in my opinion, a real philosophy behind locker rooms, and you gentlemen have had the vision to catch it. There aren't many places left in this tough world where a gang can get together with a little Turkish toweling around its middle and relax and indulge in a good old gab fest. Well, we've got it here at Happy Knoll, and those two old princes, Ned and Tim, give just the right atmosphere. Get out of a hot shower and Ned always has the bourbon ready and it's like college days again. I'm fifty years young now every time I play a round of golf. Gentlemen, don't change anything in the locker room, and with my congratulations I want to offer you an invitation. Come down and join us sometime around fivish, sixish or even sevenish, and we'll show you what a good time really is. It's about time we had a testimonial party for the Board of Governors.

Very respectfully yours,
BEN CARROW

CHAPTER XII

Breathes There a Man
with Soul So Dead

*A letter from Mr. Albert Magill, President
Emeritus of the Happy Knoll Country Club,
during his absence from that institution, to
Mr. Roger Horlick, member of the Board of
Governors.*

DEAR ROGER:

One of my purposes in traveling to foreign parts
was, by exposure to new sights and scenes, to erase
from my mind all recollection of the Happy Knoll
Country Club. It seemed to me that this would be a
simple matter, but I am sorry to say I have thought
far more frequently than necessary of Happy
Knoll. Your letters asking for financial contributions have helped in this unfortunate process. Yet
even without them, I am afraid that I still should
have wondered how large the dining room loss was
this summer, whether beetles were attacking the

17th fairway, and what was the extent of barroom breakage.

Of course, this is ridiculous. I fully realize, and I believe you do too, that the Happy Knoll Country Club is not in itself an institution of profound importance, but only a superficial manifestation of bourgeois culture. Happy Knoll and other places like it appear in the end only rather crude efforts to escape from a few of the more unpleasant realities that surround us. Why else should one play golf? Only, I think, to manufacture some artificial difficulties which are even more acute than those we leave behind us. Also, once one is on the course, it is difficult for one to be reached on the telephone. In other words, I know, and you know, that the Happy Knoll Country Club is honestly not a place meriting our serious attention.

What has it, for instance, to offer posterity? I have seen a great many ruins lately, but when its days are finished the Happy Knoll Country Club is so ephemeral that it may not be a ruin at all. Will any archeologist be able to reconstruct its golf course? I doubt it very much, even if mounds of earth are said to exist for longer than structures of brick and stone and still mark the camps of Roman legions. The clubhouse itself, being built of wood, will inevitably vanish entirely, although I have been told that Sir Arthur Evans did once find a charred fragment of a toilet seat in the Palace of Knossos at Crete, dating back to the year 1500 B.C. Doubtless the very foundations of the Happy Knoll clubhouse, including those ten-thousand-dollar buttresses under the kitchen ell, will rapidly disintegrate. The flagstone terrace by the new bar, to which I made a personal contribution of two hundred and fifty dollars, is already suffering from our winters. It is barely conceivable that portions of the swimming pool will survive, but I doubt it, when I have observed what has happened to much more elaborate ones built by Caracalla. If anything remains of Happy Knoll I predict it will be only a few drainpipes and some vestiges of septic tanks, to which no one will be able to give an accurate ascription.

Happy Knoll keeps obtruding itself on my thoughts nevertheless — in fact, to such an extent that, when I should have been examining temples and cathedrals, I have found myself searching for other Happy Knolls both in Europe and the Orient. This is obviously not a valid reason for travel; but for what it is worth, you may be interested to know that the idea of the country club has extended to many parts of the world. For instance, I had the opportunity of examining a golf course in Bangkok in Siam. I can think of no more difficult place to play golf, since in Bangkok the few pieces of land available above the water level have already been occupied by the King's Palace, some extraordinary-looking temples, and a highly confused business district. House sites in outlying parts of the city appear to have been made by digging infinite numbers of ditches or canals, known locally as Klongs. Groups of mosquitoes emerge from these Klongs each evening, and, as there seems to be no screening in Bangkok, attack the ankles; but most Bangkok residents appear oblivious to this detail. The Bangkok golf club winds about the race track so closely that it is hard to tell one from the other, and every hole contains several Klongs, bits of rice paddy and pieces of track itself.

I might speak also of an interesting course at Colombo in Ceylon situated near a crematorium that lights the premises prettily at sundown. Like the cemetery bordering our fifteenth at Happy Knoll, it is, I presume, out of bounds, and no doubt

offers Colombo Sunday golfers the same opportunities for solemn reflection that our graveyard offers us.

However, of all the courses I have seen, and these include some excellent ones in Japan, and one in Cairo which is advertised as all turf, the most intriguing still seems to me to be the Royal Hong Kong Golf Club. Hong Kong, though a city of unreality, and one which appears to exist only because the world is self-consciously looking the other way, still displays the rigid discipline which belongs to a Crown colony, and the Royal Hong Kong Golf Club, though caught in the current of change, is a worthy end-result. It is not situated on Hong Kong island, but on what is still called the New Territory, a piece of the Chinese mainland held by Great Britain on a ninety-nine-year lease from China, which started in the middle eighties of the last century. As one motors on this peninsula from the sprawling city of Kowloon toward the rigidly patrolled Anglo-Red China border, near which the Royal Hong Kong Golf Club is situated, one has many thoughts. Among these there rises the question why British businessmen and diplomats in Hong Kong, and even golfers, all share the opinion that the Generalissimo

Chiang should give up his islands of Quemoy and
Matsu, not to mention Formosa, while Hong Kong,
which was first occupied because a Chinese em-
peror objected to the British sale of Indian opium,
still remains under the Crown. But then, most of
Hong Kong is some sort of contradiction.

The road to the Royal Hong Kong Golf Club
first passes hastily built and modern textile facto-
ries, and new housing developments where bull-
dozers are unnecessary because grading can be done
more cheaply by little old Chinese ladies in black
gowns, each carrying a basket. These modern indus-
trial plants, all designed to pay for themselves in a
few years' time, due to the present trade complica-
tions of Communist China, give the Kowloon peninsula a schizophrenic quality. But as one proceeds
farther along the excellent tarmac highway these el-
ements of contrast grow gradually milder. The sea
makes jagged indentations into the high green slopes
of the peninsula, and mountainous capes and islands
rising from the water turn the surroundings into a
part of a Sung Dynasty landscape. Chinese junks,
not changed in hull or rigging since the days of
Confucius, float upon these coves, or are careened
on nearby beaches so that the owners' families can

build small fires beneath them to rid them of barnacles.

It is necessary to go straight to the border itself again to encounter the present. The New Territory and Red China are separated by a high mesh fence which stretches over miles of semitropical swampy country. Pillboxes stare at each other on either side of this border, and at night the fence is patrolled by groups of Alsatian police dogs. The chief point of communication between the West and the Bamboo Curtain lies at the intersection of the Kowloon-Canton Railroad and the boundary. Here, at a customs barrier, two sentries from the Hong Kong police and two from the Red Chinese army face each other for twenty-four hours a day. The Chinese soldiers, peasant boys not much over the age of Eagle Scouts, on the day I saw them, stood like Napoleon in Browning's poem on the Battle of Ratisbon ("neck out-thrust, you fancy how, legs wide"), each holding a Russian Burp gun at the ready — weapons which I am told are now manufactured in Canton. They wore Teutonic-looking helmets emblazoned with the Red Star of China; porous, baggy, khaki uniforms; and high brown sneakers. Their mouths gaped open in an adenoidal way.

Their expressions seemed worried rather than in-
scrutable — and at moments bewildered, for which
one could hardly blame them. Chinese countryfolk
in their straw hats and their black bombazine
moved with their identification cards quite freely
past the barrier. I particularly noticed one agile
old lady in black trotting with two buckets balanced on a pole.

"That old dear," the Hong Kong police officer
told me, "moves back and forth all day long, carrying manure to the ancestral acres."

The Royal Hong Kong Golf Club lies in close
proximity to the border. In fact I have heard that
several portions of the course are within sight of
Red China. It was almost like coming home, to see
the buildings and the grounds of the Royal Hong
Kong Golf Club, or at least like arriving in England from the Continent. There are differences between the Royal Hong Kong Golf Club and Happy
Knoll, but essentially they both spring from the
same stock.

There are, for instance, no spirit screens or court-
yards or carp ponds in front of the Royal Hong
Kong Golf Club. On the contrary, its buildings are
sternly Edwardian, like all social structures that

have been built in distant places in the shadow of the Union Jack. I could not necessarily say that the clubhouse was constructed in the lifetime of Edward the Seventh, since the architectural tradition of the Late Kipling and Pre-Somerset Maugham Period has undeviating qualities that carry straight to the present. Certainly the club buildings are very Pre-World War II, and parts of them may date even before the days when young British officers kicked footballs across no man's land in France to encourage the troops behind them, and there is still much of that spirit left at the Royal Hong Kong Golf Club. In other words, there is no nonsense about it. Even the oleander and hibiscus bushes planted sparsely about its driveway are a concession to polite convention and make no effort to be romantic, any more than do the avid women players hastening to the first tee in light but not alluring garments. The stuccoed façades are painted in a weathered, restful, seasick beige — a color which exists only in the shade of the Union Jack. For instance, if the House Committee at Happy Knoll (which in my time has done more peculiar things) should vote to have the clubhouse painted exactly this tint, they could not achieve it, because Happy

Knoll broke away from England at the time of George III. On the other hand, if Happy Knoll were in the Canadian province of Ontario the effect would be not only possible but inevitable.

This homelike appearance, this illusion of a home away from home, is not in the least marred by the Chinese attendants, who like all their race have been quick to adopt the coloration of other cultures. A sign on the driveway greets the visitor announcing both in English and Chinese characters that hawkers are not allowed, and a subtitle to the sign enlarges the statement that the hawking of golf balls is prohibited. This shows the alertness of the Greens Committee of the Royal Hong Kong Golf Club. I could not help thinking that such a sign would delight Benny Muldoon, whom I have often heard advance the theory that golfers at Happy Knoll should start each game with a brand-new ball in the price range of over a dollar and fifty cents, and that no caddy should be allowed ever to sell a secondhand golf ball to a player. It is a habit which encourages immorality in caddies in their most formative years, and how can a golf pro raise a family if the golf shop is not patronized?

In my experience it always happens that, whenever one leaves home, every place is in the midst of its rainy season. The Royal Hong Kong Golf Club was no exception. Though the course was too wet for serious play, it did not dampen the enthusiasm of a number of foursomes who must, from their girth and ruddy features, have been high executives in the Hong Kong and Shanghai Bank, or junior partners in the old importing firm of Jardine and Mathison. The moist and cloudy weather did not deter the greens keepers either. It was interesting to see a number of Chinese with lawnmowers, one pushing and one pulling, and together achieving results as excellent as we manage at Happy Knoll with an internal combustion engine. The fairways of the Royal Hong Kong Golf Club are not a problem either, because they are kept grazed by herds of docile Oriental cattle. They move away politely from the tees. They never graze on the greens either, because an old gentleman in shorts appears from behind a bamboo bush at critical moments. When I asked why under the sun the Royal Hong Kong Golf Course was established so far away from anywhere, I was informed that, because of the New Territory's heavy rural population, the golf course had to be established in moderately hilly and untillable country. Thus the Royal Hong Kong course is in the foothills where the past mingles with the present in the form of crockery burial urns that are grouped along many fairways. It is well, I was also told, to allow the caddies to look for balls in the rough without assistance, because of occasional cobras and other snakes, although these on the whole are shy and of a mild disposition.

Details of the Royal Hong Kong Golf Club obviously differ from those of Happy Knoll, but essentially the problems are the same; for instance that paramount one of membership. As you and I both know, you cannot maintain a golf club without members, and yet they must still be screened somehow. Of late years there have been some complaints regarding new acquisitions to the roster of Happy Knoll, and the same is doubtless true of the Royal Hong Kong Golf Club, where residents from the foreign colony form a cosmopolitan membership that must at times be complicated. Chinese women, by the way, I am told are the most enthusiastic golfers in Hong Kong. There is also the constant problem of suitable clothing. In Hong Kong as in Happy Knoll it seems that slacks grow shorter and tighter annually — which makes me wonder what steps our Board of Governors are taking this year. This problem, however, is not as acute as it is at Happy Knoll, for a very excellent reason. The Royal Hong Kong Golf Club consists of two buildings: a large and handsome one for men, and a smaller one for women. Women, I am told, are not allowed to enter the men's building on any pretext whatsoever. How much happier things would be at Happy Knoll if our house committee had had the character to adhere to a similar strict rule before it was too late! There was a time when no woman or child was allowed on the south veranda of Happy Knoll. It is nothing but a play-pen now. I suppose the Pendleton Room will be opened next.

From the point of view of personal attention and eagerness I must admit that the bar of the Royal Hong Kong Golf Club, in either the men's or the women's sections, is vastly superior to ours at Happy Knoll because of the large number of assiduous and intelligent Chinese attendants. Indeed the constant and skilled personal attention which one receives in the Orient in such unstinted measure is a reason why some Europeans remain away from home permanently. When I think of Chuck and Bill, those two boys we employ in the summer to pass drinks at

Happy Knoll, and who only do it to pay their college tuition, and who never appear when they are called because part of their contract is to have golf lessons, the trip to the Red China border seems very much worth while. I will say, however, that a Royal Hong Kong jigger seems only about a third of what we use at Happy Knoll — or else, like other Europeans in the Orient, the climate may be driving me to drink. As I sat with my fourth Scotch-and-soda, thinking that one of Old Ned's would have served the same purpose and wondering how Kipling's gentlemen-rankers could ever have become intoxicated, I was struck by one further phenomenon. Fishnets with netting about one inch square were draped in front of all the windows of the comfortable club lounge. When I inquired whether these were intended to protect members from golf balls I was told that they were a device employed by the British to keep out flies. When I asked how such a large mesh could stop flies I was told that the netting confused these insects, and that the same idea was used successfully by the British in various parts of Cairo. I was about to say that this netting was not unlike some aspects of the British foreign policy, but I refrained, being a guest of the Crown. Instead

I spent some time observing the confusion of the flies, but not all of them were puzzled. Four, while I watched, passed through the net and lighted trustfully upon the saucer of salted peanuts that are

served with Scotch-and-soda. You may not believe this, but then a great many people did not believe Marco Polo either, until recent researchers proved him to be very accurate.

Yet I must say in the midst of this scientific observation a spasm of nostalgia came over me. It is great to dream in Venice and fine to study in Rome, but when it comes to living perhaps, after all, there is no place like home, or at least one has become accustomed to it. I wish that, as I write these lines, I were back at Happy Knoll; but don't post this on the bulletin board, or someone may ask me to make up another deficit.

Sincerely yours,
ALBERT MAGILL